2nd Conference of the Asia-Pacific Chapter of the Association for Computational Linguistics and the 12th International Joint Conference on Natural Language Processing (AACL-IJCNLP 2022)

Tutorial Abstracts

Online
20-21 November 2022

ISBN: 978-1-7138-6313-7

Printed from e-media with permission by:

Curran Associates, Inc.
57 Morehouse Lane
Red Hook, NY 12571

CURRAN ASSOCIATES INC. proceedings.com

Some format issues inherent in the e-media version may also appear in this print version.

Printed with permission by Curran Associates, Inc. (2023)

For permission requests, please contact the Association for Computational Linguistics at the address below.

Association for Computational Linguistics
209 N. Eighth Street
Stroudsburg, Pennsylvania 18360

Phone: 1-570-476-8006
Fax: 1-570-476-0860

acl@aclweb.org

Additional copies of this publication are available from:

Curran Associates, Inc.
57 Morehouse Lane
Red Hook, NY 12571 USA
Phone: 845-758-0400
Fax: 845-758-2633
Email: curran@proceedings.com
Web: www.proceedings.com

AACL-IJCNLP 2022

The 2nd Conference of the Asia-Pacific Chapter of the Association for Computational Linguistics and the 12th International Joint Conference on Natural Language Processing

Tutorial Abstracts

November 20 - 21, 2022

Order copies of this and other ACL proceedings from:

Association for Computational Linguistics (ACL)
209 N. Eighth Street
Stroudsburg, PA 18360
USA
Tel: +1-570-476-8006
Fax: +1-570-476-0860
acl@aclweb.org

Message from the Tutorial Chairs

Welcome to the Tutorials Session of AACL-IJCNLP 2022.

The AACL-IJCNLP tutorials session is organized to give conference attendees a comprehensive introduction by expert researchers to some topics of importance drawn from our rapidly growing and changing research field.

The call, submission, reviewing and selection of tutorials were carried out by the tutorial chairs. The selection criteria were based on clarity and preparedness; novelty or timely character of the topic, interest for Asia-Pacific NLP community; instructors' experience; likely audience interest; open access of the tutorial instructional material; and diversity and inclusion.

A total of 14 tutorial submissions were received, of which 6 were selected for presentation at AACL-IJCNLP. We solicited two types of tutorials, namely cutting-edge themes and introductory themes. The 6 tutorials for ACL include an introductory tutorial, a tutorial combining introductory and cutting edge contents, and six cutting-edge tutorials. The introductory tutorial is dedicated to pre-trained models for Cantonese language. The tutorial on knowledge graph construction deals with both kinds of theme. The cutting-edge tutorials address situated reasoning, the effectiveness of pre-trained language models, multilingual semantics, and misinformation and media bias.

We would like to thank the authors of the tutorials for their contribution and flexibility in organizing the conference, which went from initially face-to-face to hybrid mode and finally to fully online mode. Our thanks go to the conference organizers for effective collaboration, in particular to the general chair Yulan He.

We hope you enjoy the tutorials.

AACL-IJCNLP 2022 Tutorial Co-chairs
Miguel A. Alonso
Zhongyu Wei

Organizing Committee

Tutorial Co-Chairs

Miguel A. Alonso, Universidade da Coruña, Spain
Zhongyu Wei, Fudan University, China

Table of Contents

Efficient and Robust Knowledge Graph Construction

Ningyu Zhang[1], Tao Gui[2], Guoshun Nan[3],
[1]Zhejiang University & AZFT Joint Lab for Knowledge Engine, China
[2]Institute of Modern Languages and Linguistics, Fudan University, China
[3]Beijing University of Posts and Telecommunications, China
zhangningyu@zju.edu.cn, tgui@fudan.edu.cn, nanguo2021@bupt.edu.cn

Abstract

Knowledge graph construction which aims to extract knowledge from the text corpus, has appealed to the NLP community researchers. Previous decades have witnessed the remarkable progress of knowledge graph construction on the basis of neural models; however, those models often cost massive computation or labeled data resources and suffer from unstable inference accounting for biased or adversarial samples. Recently, numerous approaches have been explored to mitigate the efficiency and robustness issues for knowledge graph construction, such as prompt learning and adversarial training. In this tutorial, we aim to bring interested NLP researchers up to speed on the recent and ongoing techniques for efficient and robust knowledge graph construction. Additionally, our goal is to provide a systematic and up-to-date overview of these methods and reveal new research opportunities to the audience.

1 Introduction

Motivation: Knowledge Graphs (KGs) regard the knowledge as fact triples in the form of `<subject, predicate, object>`, which can benefit a wide range of natural language processing tasks including question answering (Jia et al., 2021; Fei et al., 2022; Zhang et al., 2021a), fact verification (Zhou et al., 2019), data-to-text generation (Li et al., 2021), commonsense reasoning (Bosselut et al., 2019) and so on. Knowledge graph construction tasks including Named Entity Recognition (NER) (Gui et al., 2019), Relation Extraction (RE) (Zeng et al., 2015) target to extract structural information from unstructured texts, have appealed to researchers in NLP community. While those researchers have largely separated approaches from tasks, they have encountered similar issues such as efficiency and robustness.

Intuitively, efficient and robust knowledge graph construction has been widely investigated due to its potential value of making models scenario-adaptable, data-efficient, and particularly convenient for real-world applications with cold-start issues. In this tutorial, we take a holistic view of knowledge graph construction, introducing the commonalities in the issues and solutions regarding efficiency and robustness. We will explore the approaches of named entity recognition and relation extraction with few-shot labeled data, limited computation resources and approaches to improve the model robustness.

Note that our tutorial is related to green deep learning (Xu et al., 2021) that appeals to researchers to focus on carbon emission and energy usage during model training and inference, and relevant to robust NLP (Omar et al., 2022) which focuses on addressing issues in current models' language understanding capabilities with adversarial attacks. Meanwhile, trends within knowledge graph construction have shifted toward low-resource rather than considering massive labeled data and reliable & trustworthy knowledge graph construction. Notably, it is worth considering the knowledge graph construction tasks as a whole to develop methodologies for efficiency and robustness issues. We will discuss these works and suggest avenues in the future.

Tutorial Content: We will start this tutorial by defining tasks of knowledge graph construction, including named entity recognition relation extraction from sentences or documents. Then, we will give introductions to the basic models, open datasets and tools used in knowledge graph construction covering both English and Chinese (Zhang et al., 2022). We plan to focus on methods that enable efficient knowledge graph construction, such as the distant supervision (Wang et al., 2022b) and data augmentation paradigms of creating training data (Liu et al., 2021), model enhancement methods like meta-learning (Yu et al., 2020), transfer learning (Ma et al., 2022a) and prompt learn-

Proceedings of the 2nd Conference of the Asia-Pacific Chapter of the Association for Computational Linguistics and the 12th International Joint Conference on Natural Language Processing: Tutorial Abstracts, pages 1–7
November 20-21, 2022.

ing (Chen et al., 2022d,c,b), parameter-efficient approaches (Ma et al., 2022b; Chen et al., 2022a), including adaptor-based tuning. We will then explore research focusing on robust knowledge graph construction for stable learning with adversarial attacks and selection or semantic biases.

During the tutorial, we plan to deliver lessons learned from the diverse communities involved in knowledge graph construction research and will introduce insights from the industry when building a business knowledge graph in low-resource settings. Section 3 has an outline of tutorial content.

Tutorial slides will be available at `https://github.com/NLP-Tutorials/AACL-IJCNLP2022-KGC-Tutorial`.

Relevance to AACL: Knowledge graphs benefit many crucial NLP tasks, and knowledge graph construction tasks such as relation extraction and named entity recognition are core tasks in information extraction. A 2018 NAACL tutorial, "Scalable Construction and Reasoning of Massive Knowledge Bases" (Ren et al., 2018), introduced a summary of recent KB, and IE works. More recently, an ACL tutorial, "Multi-modal Information Extraction from Text, Semi-structured, and Tabular Data on the Web" (Dong et al., 2020), provided an overview of information extraction (IE) from Web data with two vital dimensions: the thrust to develop scalable approaches and the diversity in data modality. However, previous tutorials mainly focus on models with rich resources of labeled data and computation, and recent years have witnessed the fast development of efficient and robust knowledge graph construction. On the other hand, the NLP community has paid much attention to robust NLP, such as an EMNLP 2021 tutorial, "Robustness and Adversarial Examples in Natural Language Processing" (Chang et al., 2021). Different from this tutorial in general NLP, we target a small, focused domain of knowledge graph construction and introduce the detailed latest work in limited 3 hours.

2 Type of this Tutorial

This tutorial contains **cutting-edge** approaches in general knowledge graph construction approaches regarding efficiency and robustness issues. However, our coverage of this tutorial will contain **introductory material** of knowledge graph construction for widespread audiences of the NLP community. Besides, we will introduce methods of Chinese knowledge graph construction for Asia audiences.

3 Outline

1. (1 hour) Introduction and Applications

- Named Entity Recognition (NER)
  - Flat NER (Li et al., 2020)
  - Nested NER (Straková et al., 2019)
  - Joint Flat and Nested NER (Wang and Lu, 2020)
- Relation Extraction
  - Supervised Relation Extraction (Lin et al., 2016; Song et al., 2018; Nan et al., 2021)
  - Distance-supervised Relation extraction (Zeng et al., 2015)
  - Open Relation Extraction (Wu et al., 2019; Zhao et al., 2021)
- Knowledge Graph Construction
  - Introduction (Bosselut et al., 2019)
  - Industry Examples
  - Resource Applications and Toolkits
  - Importance of the Efficiency and Robustness

2. (1 hour) Efficient KG Construction

- Data Efficiency
  - Data Augmentation (Chaudhary et al., 2019)
  - Model Enhancement (Chen et al., 2022d)
  - Hybrid Approaches (Hu et al., 2021)
- Model Efficiency
  - Parameter-efficient Learning (Zhou et al., 2021)
  - Efficient Architecture (Zhu, 2021)
- Inference Efficiency
  - Generative Inference (Yan et al., 2021)
  - Non-autoregressive Decoding (Sui et al., 2021)

3. (1 hour) Robust KG Construction

- Robustness Problem Discovery
  - Model Behavior Probing (Cao et al., 2021)
  - Robustness Evaluation (Wang et al., 2021)

- Data Correction
  - Data Denoising (Ma et al., 2021)
  - Data Bias Removal (Mehrabi et al., 2020)
- Robust Model Learning
  - Adversarial Training (Li and Qiu, 2021; Liu et al., 2022)
  - Robust Architecture Design (Zheng et al., 2022; Wang et al., 2022a)
  - Causal Inference (Zhang et al., 2021b)

4 Prerequisites

Anyone with a background in natural language processing can access this tutorial. Moreover, a basic understanding of neural networks, preferably with some knowledge of information extraction, knowledge graph, and pre-trained language models, is helpful.

5 Reading list

- "Knowledge Vault: A Web-Scale Approach to Probabilistic Knowledge Fusion", (Dong et al., 2014)
- "Fonduer: Knowledge Base Construction from Richly Formatted Data", (Wu et al., 2018)
- "A Survey on Recent Approaches for Natural Language Processing in Low-Resource Scenarios", (Hedderich et al., 2021)
- "Few-Shot Named Entity Recognition: An Empirical Baseline Study", (Huang et al., 2021)
- "Knowledge Extraction in Low-Resource Scenarios: Survey and Perspective", (Deng et al., 2022)
- "Uncertainty-Aware Label Refinement for Sequence Labeling ", (Gui et al., 2020)
- "Reasoning with latent structure refinement for document-level relation extraction", (Nan et al., 2020)
- "KnowPrompt: Knowledge-aware Prompt-tuning with Synergistic Optimization for Relation Extraction", (Chen et al., 2022d)

6 Presenters

Ningyu Zhang is an associate professor at Zhejiang University, leading the group about KG and NLP technologies. He is also a researcher at Alibaba-Zhejiang University Joint Research Institute of Frontier Technologies (AZFT), Co-PI of the Alibaba Open Business Knowledge Graph[1], which is devoted to benefiting e-commerce applications and to discovering socioeconomic values. He is a member of ACL, a member of the Youth Working Committee of the Chinese Information Processing Society of China, and the member of the Language and Knowledge Computing Professional Committee of the Chinese Information Processing Society of China. He has published many papers in top international academic conferences and journals such as ICLR, ACL, ENNLP, NAACL, and IEEE/ACM Transactions on Audio Speech and Language. He has served as PCs for NeurIPS, ICLR, KDD, ICML, AAAI, IJCAI and reviewer for ARR, TKDE, and TKDD. He has received the best paper award from the China Conference on Knowledge Graph and Semantic Computing and the best paper nominations from the International Joint Conference on Knowledge Graphs. He has won first place in the TREC Precision Medicine 2020 sponsored by the National Institute of Standards and Technology (NIST) and fourth place in the international semantic evaluation competition (SemEval 2021 Task4) sponsored by ACL. He has given multiple talks on information extraction and knowledge graph.

Email: `zhangningyu@zju.edu.cn`

Homepage: `https://person.zju.edu.cn/en/ningyu`

Tao Gui is an associate professor at the Institute of Modern Languages and Linguistics of Fudan University. He is the key member of the FudanNLP group[2]. He is a member of ACL, a member of the Youth Working Committee of the Chinese Information Processing Society of China, and the member of the Language and Knowledge Computing Professional Committee of the Chinese Information Processing Society of China. He has published more than 40 papers in top international academic conferences and journals such as ACL, ENNLP, AAAI, IJCAI, SIGIR, and so on. He has served as area chair or PCs for SIGIR, AAAI, IJCAI, TPAMI, and ARR. He has received the Outstanding Doctoral Dissertation Award of the Chinese Informa-

[1] `https://kg.alibaba.com/`

[2] `https://nlp.fudan.edu.cn`

tion Processing Society of China, the area chair favorite Award of COLING 2018, the outstanding Paper Award of NLPCC 2019, and a scholar of young talent promoting projects of CAST.

Email: tgui@fudan.edu.cn

Homepage: https://guitaowufeng.github.io

Guoshun Nan is a tenure-track professor in the School of Cyber Science and Engineering, Beijing University of Posts and Telecommunications (BUPT). He is a key member of the National Engineering Research Center of Mobile Network Security and a member of the Wireless Technology Innovation Institute of BUPT. Before starting his academic career, he also worked in Hewlett-Packard Company (China) for more than four years as an engineer. He is a member of ACL. He has a broad interest in information extraction, model robustness, multimodal retrieval, cyber security and the next generation of wireless networks. He has published more than ten papers in top-tier conferences such as ACL, CVPR, EMNLP, SIGIR, IJCAI, CKIM and Sigcomm. He served as a reviewer for ACL, EMNLP, AAAI, IJCAI, Neurocomputing and IEEE Transaction on Image Processing.

Email: nanguo2021@bupt.edu.cn

References

Antoine Bosselut, Hannah Rashkin, Maarten Sap, Chaitanya Malaviya, Asli Celikyilmaz, and Yejin Choi. 2019. COMET: Commonsense transformers for automatic knowledge graph construction. In *Proceedings of the 57th Annual Meeting of the Association for Computational Linguistics*, pages 4762–4779, Florence, Italy. Association for Computational Linguistics.

Boxi Cao, Hongyu Lin, Xianpei Han, Le Sun, Lingyong Yan, Meng Liao, Tong Xue, and Jin Xu. 2021. Knowledgeable or educated guess? revisiting language models as knowledge bases. In *Proceedings of the 59th Annual Meeting of the Association for Computational Linguistics and the 11th International Joint Conference on Natural Language Processing, ACL/IJCNLP 2021, (Volume 1: Long Papers), Virtual Event, August 1-6, 2021*, pages 1860–1874. Association for Computational Linguistics.

Kai-Wei Chang, He He, Robin Jia, and Sameer Singh. 2021. Robustness and adversarial examples in natural language processing. In *Proceedings of the 2021 Conference on Empirical Methods in Natural Language Processing: Tutorial Abstracts*, pages 22–26, Punta Cana, Dominican Republic & Online. Association for Computational Linguistics.

Aditi Chaudhary, Jiateng Xie, Zaid Sheikh, Graham Neubig, and Jaime G. Carbonell. 2019. A little annotation does a lot of good: A study in bootstrapping low-resource named entity recognizers. In *Proceedings of the 2019 Conference on Empirical Methods in Natural Language Processing and the 9th International Joint Conference on Natural Language Processing, EMNLP-IJCNLP 2019, Hong Kong, China, November 3-7, 2019*, pages 5163–5173. Association for Computational Linguistics.

Xiang Chen, Lei Li, Shumin Deng, Chuanqi Tan, Changliang Xu, Fei Huang, Luo Si, Huajun Chen, and Ningyu Zhang. 2022a. Lightner: A lightweight tuning paradigm for low-resource ner via pluggable prompting. In *Proceedings of the 29th International Conference on Computational Linguistics*. International Committee on Computational Linguistics.

Xiang Chen, Lei Li, Ningyu Zhang, Xiaozhuan Liang, Shumin Deng, Chuanqi Tan, Fei Huang, Luo Si, and Huajun Chen. 2022b. Decoupling knowledge from memorization: Retrieval-augmented prompt learning. In *Advances in Neural Information Processing Systems (NeurIPS)*.

Xiang Chen, Lei Li, Ningyu Zhang, Chuanqi Tan, Fei Huang, Luo Si, and Huajun Chen. 2022c. Relation extraction as open-book examination: Retrieval-enhanced prompt tuning. In *SIGIR '22: The 45th International ACM SIGIR Conference on Research and Development in Information Retrieval, Madrid, Spain, July 11 - 15, 2022*, pages 2443–2448. ACM.

Xiang Chen, Ningyu Zhang, Xin Xie, Shumin Deng, Yunzhi Yao, Chuanqi Tan, Fei Huang, Luo Si, and Huajun Chen. 2022d. Knowprompt: Knowledge-aware prompt-tuning with synergistic optimization for relation extraction. In *WWW '22: The ACM Web Conference 2022, Virtual Event, Lyon, France, April 25 - 29, 2022*, pages 2778–2788. ACM.

Shumin Deng, Ningyu Zhang, Hui Chen, Feiyu Xiong, Jeff Z. Pan, and Huajun Chen. 2022. Knowledge extraction in low-resource scenarios: Survey and perspective. *CoRR*, abs/2202.08063.

Xin Dong, Evgeniy Gabrilovich, Geremy Heitz, Wilko Horn, Ni Lao, Kevin Murphy, Thomas Strohmann, Shaohua Sun, and Wei Zhang. 2014. Knowledge vault: a web-scale approach to probabilistic knowledge fusion. In *The 20th ACM SIGKDD International Conference on Knowledge Discovery and Data Mining, KDD '14, New York, NY, USA - August 24 - 27, 2014*, pages 601–610. ACM.

Xin Luna Dong, Hannaneh Hajishirzi, Colin Lockard, and Prashant Shiralkar. 2020. Multi-modal information extraction from text, semi-structured, and tabular data on the web. In *Proceedings of the 58th Annual Meeting of the Association for Computational Linguistics: Tutorial Abstracts*, pages 23–26, Online. Association for Computational Linguistics.

Zichu Fei, Qi Zhang, Tao Gui, Di Liang, Sirui Wang, Wei Wu, and Xuan-Jing Huang. 2022. Cqg: A simple and effective controlled generation framework for multi-hop question generation. In *Proceedings of the 60th Annual Meeting of the Association for Computational Linguistics (Volume 1: Long Papers)*, pages 6896–6906.

Tao Gui, Jiacheng Ye, Qi Zhang, Zhengyan Li, Zichu Fei, Yeyun Gong, and Xuan-Jing Huang. 2020. Uncertainty-aware label refinement for sequence labeling. In *Proceedings of the 2020 Conference on Empirical Methods in Natural Language Processing (EMNLP)*, pages 2316–2326.

Tao Gui, Yicheng Zou, Qi Zhang, Minlong Peng, Jinlan Fu, Zhongyu Wei, and Xuanjing Huang. 2019. A lexicon-based graph neural network for Chinese NER. In *Proceedings of the 2019 Conference on Empirical Methods in Natural Language Processing and the 9th International Joint Conference on Natural Language Processing (EMNLP-IJCNLP)*, pages 1040–1050, Hong Kong, China. Association for Computational Linguistics.

Michael A. Hedderich, Lukas Lange, Heike Adel, Jannik Strötgen, and Dietrich Klakow. 2021. A survey on recent approaches for natural language processing in low-resource scenarios. In *Proceedings of the 2021 Conference of the North American Chapter of the Association for Computational Linguistics: Human Language Technologies, NAACL-HLT 2021, Online, June 6-11, 2021*, pages 2545–2568. Association for Computational Linguistics.

Xuming Hu, Chenwei Zhang, Yawen Yang, Xiaohe Li, Li Lin, Lijie Wen, and Philip S. Yu. 2021. Gradient imitation reinforcement learning for low resource relation extraction. In *Proceedings of the 2021 Conference on Empirical Methods in Natural Language Processing, EMNLP 2021, Virtual Event / Punta Cana, Dominican Republic, 7-11 November, 2021*, pages 2737–2746. Association for Computational Linguistics.

Jiaxin Huang, Chunyuan Li, Krishan Subudhi, Damien Jose, Shobana Balakrishnan, Weizhu Chen, Baolin Peng, Jianfeng Gao, and Jiawei Han. 2021. Few-shot named entity recognition: An empirical baseline study. In *Proceedings of the 2021 Conference on Empirical Methods in Natural Language Processing, EMNLP 2021, Virtual Event / Punta Cana, Dominican Republic, 7-11 November, 2021*, pages 10408–10423. Association for Computational Linguistics.

Zhen Jia, Soumajit Pramanik, Rishiraj Saha Roy, and Gerhard Weikum. 2021. Complex temporal question answering on knowledge graphs. In *CIKM '21: The 30th ACM International Conference on Information and Knowledge Management, Virtual Event, Queensland, Australia, November 1 - 5, 2021*, pages 792–802. ACM.

Junyi Li, Tianyi Tang, Wayne Xin Zhao, Zhicheng Wei, Nicholas Jing Yuan, and Ji-Rong Wen. 2021. Few-shot knowledge graph-to-text generation with pretrained language models. In *Findings of the Association for Computational Linguistics: ACL-IJCNLP 2021*, pages 1558–1568, Online. Association for Computational Linguistics.

Linyang Li and Xipeng Qiu. 2021. Token-aware virtual adversarial training in natural language understanding. *Proceedings of the AAAI Conference on Artificial Intelligence*, 35(9):8410–8418.

Xiaonan Li, Hang Yan, Xipeng Qiu, and Xuanjing Huang. 2020. FLAT: chinese NER using flat-lattice transformer. In *Proceedings of the 58th Annual Meeting of the Association for Computational Linguistics, ACL 2020, Online, July 5-10, 2020*, pages 6836–6842. Association for Computational Linguistics.

Yankai Lin, Shiqi Shen, Zhiyuan Liu, Huanbo Luan, and Maosong Sun. 2016. Neural relation extraction with selective attention over instances. In *Proceedings of the 54th Annual Meeting of the Association for Computational Linguistics, ACL 2016, August 7-12, 2016, Berlin, Germany, Volume 1: Long Papers*. The Association for Computer Linguistics.

Kun Liu, Yao Fu, Chuanqi Tan, Mosha Chen, Ningyu Zhang, Songfang Huang, and Sheng Gao. 2021. Noisy-labeled NER with confidence estimation. In *Proceedings of the 2021 Conference of the North American Chapter of the Association for Computational Linguistics: Human Language Technologies, NAACL-HLT 2021, Online, June 6-11, 2021*, pages 3437–3445. Association for Computational Linguistics.

Qin Liu, Rui Zheng, Bao Rong, Jingyi Liu, Zhihua Liu, Zhanzhan Cheng, Liang Qiao, Tao Gui, Qi Zhang, and Xuan-Jing Huang. 2022. Flooding-x: Improving bert's resistance to adversarial attacks via loss-restricted fine-tuning. In *Proceedings of the 60th Annual Meeting of the Association for Computational Linguistics (Volume 1: Long Papers)*, pages 5634–5644.

Ruotian Ma, Tao Gui, Linyang Li, Qi Zhang, Xuanjing Huang, and Yaqian Zhou. 2021. SENT: sentence-level distant relation extraction via negative training. In *Proceedings of the 59th Annual Meeting of the Association for Computational Linguistics and the 11th International Joint Conference on Natural Language Processing, ACL/IJCNLP 2021, (Volume 1: Long Papers), Virtual Event, August 1-6, 2021*, pages 6201–6213. Association for Computational Linguistics.

Ruotian Ma, Yiding Tan, Xin Zhou, Xuanting Chen, Di Liang, Sirui Wang, Wei Wu, and Tao Gui. 2022a. Searching for optimal subword tokenization in cross-domain ner. In *Proceedings of the Thirty-First International Joint Conference on Artificial Intelligence, IJCAI-22*, pages 4289–4295. International Joint Conferences on Artificial Intelligence Organization. Main Track.

Ruotian Ma, Xin Zhou, Tao Gui, Yiding Tan, Linyang Li, Qi Zhang, and Xuanjing Huang. 2022b. Template-free prompt tuning for few-shot NER. In *Proceedings of the 2022 Conference of the North American Chapter of the Association for Computational Linguistics: Human Language Technologies*, pages 5721–5732, Seattle, United States. Association for Computational Linguistics.

Ninareh Mehrabi, Thamme Gowda, Fred Morstatter, Nanyun Peng, and Aram Galstyan. 2020. Man is to person as woman is to location: Measuring gender bias in named entity recognition. In *HT '20: 31st ACM Conference on Hypertext and Social Media, Virtual Event, USA, July 13-15, 2020*, pages 231–232. ACM.

Guoshun Nan, Zhijiang Guo, Ivan Sekulic, and Wei Lu. 2020. Reasoning with latent structure refinement for document-level relation extraction. In *Proceedings of the 58th Annual Meeting of the Association for Computational Linguistics, ACL 2020, Online, July 5-10, 2020*, pages 1546–1557. Association for Computational Linguistics.

Guoshun Nan, Jiaqi Zeng, Rui Qiao, Zhijiang Guo, and Wei Lu. 2021. Uncovering main causalities for long-tailed information extraction. In *Proceedings of the 2021 Conference on Empirical Methods in Natural Language Processing*, pages 9683–9695.

Marwan Omar, Soohyeon Choi, Daehun Nyang, and David Mohaisen. 2022. Robust natural language processing: Recent advances, challenges, and future directions. *IEEE Access*, 10:86038–86056.

Xiang Ren, Nanyun Peng, and William Yang Wang. 2018. Scalable construction and reasoning of massive knowledge bases. In *Proceedings of the 2018 Conference of the North American Chapter of the Association for Computational Linguistics: Tutorial Abstracts*, pages 10–16, New Orleans, Louisiana. Association for Computational Linguistics.

Linfeng Song, Yue Zhang, Zhiguo Wang, and Daniel Gildea. 2018. N-ary relation extraction using graph-state lstm. In *Proceedings of the 2018 Conference on Empirical Methods in Natural Language Processing*, pages 2226–2235.

Jana Straková, Milan Straka, and Jan Hajic. 2019. Neural architectures for nested NER through linearization. In *Proceedings of the 57th Conference of the Association for Computational Linguistics, ACL 2019, Florence, Italy, July 28- August 2, 2019, Volume 1: Long Papers*, pages 5326–5331. Association for Computational Linguistics.

Dianbo Sui, Chenhao Wang, Yubo Chen, Kang Liu, Jun Zhao, and Wei Bi. 2021. Set generation networks for end-to-end knowledge base population. In *Proceedings of the 2021 Conference on Empirical Methods in Natural Language Processing, EMNLP 2021, Virtual Event / Punta Cana, Dominican Republic, 7-11 November, 2021*, pages 9650–9660. Association for Computational Linguistics.

Jue Wang and Wei Lu. 2020. Two are better than one: Joint entity and relation extraction with table-sequence encoders. In *Proceedings of the 2020 Conference on Empirical Methods in Natural Language Processing, EMNLP 2020, Online, November 16-20, 2020*, pages 1706–1721. Association for Computational Linguistics.

Xiao Wang, Shihan Dou, Limao Xiong, Yicheng Zou, Qi Zhang, Tao Gui, Liang Qiao, Zhanzhan Cheng, and Xuan-Jing Huang. 2022a. Miner: Improving out-of-vocabulary named entity recognition from an information theoretic perspective. In *Proceedings of the 60th Annual Meeting of the Association for Computational Linguistics (Volume 1: Long Papers)*, pages 5590–5600.

Xiao Wang, Qin Liu, Tao Gui, Qi Zhang, Yicheng Zou, Xin Zhou, Jiacheng Ye, Yongxin Zhang, Rui Zheng, Zexiong Pang, Qinzhuo Wu, Zhengyan Li, Chong Zhang, Ruotian Ma, Zichu Fei, Ruijian Cai, Jun Zhao, Xingwu Hu, Zhiheng Yan, Yiding Tan, Yuan Hu, Qiyuan Bian, Zhihua Liu, Shan Qin, Bolin Zhu, Xiaoyu Xing, Jinlan Fu, Yue Zhang, Minlong Peng, Xiaoqing Zheng, Yaqian Zhou, Zhongyu Wei, Xipeng Qiu, and Xuanjing Huang. 2021. TextFlint: Unified multilingual robustness evaluation toolkit for natural language processing. In *Proceedings of the 59th Annual Meeting of the Association for Computational Linguistics and the 11th International Joint Conference on Natural Language Processing: System Demonstrations*, pages 347–355, Online. Association for Computational Linguistics.

Zifeng Wang, Rui Wen, Xi Chen, Shao-Lun Huang, Ningyu Zhang, and Yefeng Zheng. 2022b. Finding influential instances for distantly supervised relation extraction. In *Proceedings of the 29th International Conference on Computational Linguistics*.

Ruidong Wu, Yuan Yao, Xu Han, Ruobing Xie, Zhiyuan Liu, Fen Lin, Leyu Lin, and Maosong Sun. 2019. Open relation extraction: Relational knowledge transfer from supervised data to unsupervised data. In *Proceedings of the 2019 Conference on Empirical Methods in Natural Language Processing and the 9th International Joint Conference on Natural Language Processing (EMNLP-IJCNLP)*, pages 219–228, Hong Kong, China. Association for Computational Linguistics.

Sen Wu, Luke Hsiao, Xiao Cheng, Braden Hancock, Theodoros Rekatsinas, Philip Alexander Levis, and Christopher Ré. 2018. Fonduer: Knowledge base construction from richly formatted data. In *Proceedings of the 2018 International Conference on Management of Data, SIGMOD Conference 2018, Houston, TX, USA, June 10-15, 2018*, pages 1301–1316. ACM.

Jingjing Xu, Wangchunshu Zhou, Zhiyi Fu, Hao Zhou, and Lei Li. 2021. A survey on green deep learning. *arXiv preprint arXiv:2111.05193*.

Hang Yan, Tao Gui, Junqi Dai, Qipeng Guo, Zheng Zhang, and Xipeng Qiu. 2021. A unified generative framework for various NER subtasks. In *Proceedings of the 59th Annual Meeting of the Association for Computational Linguistics and the 11th International Joint Conference on Natural Language Processing, ACL/IJCNLP 2021, (Volume 1: Long Papers), Virtual Event, August 1-6, 2021*, pages 5808–5822. Association for Computational Linguistics.

Haiyang Yu, Ningyu Zhang, Shumin Deng, Hongbin Ye, Wei Zhang, and Huajun Chen. 2020. Bridging text and knowledge with multi-prototype embedding for few-shot relational triple extraction. In *Proceedings of the 28th International Conference on Computational Linguistics*, pages 6399–6410, Barcelona, Spain (Online). International Committee on Computational Linguistics.

Daojian Zeng, Kang Liu, Yubo Chen, and Jun Zhao. 2015. Distant supervision for relation extraction via piecewise convolutional neural networks. In *Proceedings of the 2015 Conference on Empirical Methods in Natural Language Processing*, pages 1753–1762, Lisbon, Portugal. Association for Computational Linguistics.

Ningyu Zhang, Qianghuai Jia, Shumin Deng, Xiang Chen, Hongbin Ye, Hui Chen, Huaixiao Tou, Gang Huang, Zhao Wang, Nengwei Hua, and Huajun Chen. 2021a. Alicg: Fine-grained and evolvable conceptual graph construction for semantic search at alibaba. In *KDD '21: The 27th ACM SIGKDD Conference on Knowledge Discovery and Data Mining, Virtual Event, Singapore, August 14-18, 2021*, pages 3895–3905. ACM.

Ningyu Zhang, Xin Xu, Liankuan Tao, Haiyang Yu, Hongbin Ye, Shuofei Qiao, Xin Xie, Xiang Chen, Zhoubo Li, Lei Li, et al. 2022. Deepke: A deep learning based knowledge extraction toolkit for knowledge base population. *arXiv preprint arXiv:2201.03335*.

Wenkai Zhang, Hongyu Lin, Xianpei Han, and Le Sun. 2021b. De-biasing distantly supervised named entity recognition via causal intervention. In *Proceedings of the 59th Annual Meeting of the Association for Computational Linguistics and the 11th International Joint Conference on Natural Language Processing, ACL/IJCNLP 2021, (Volume 1: Long Papers), Virtual Event, August 1-6, 2021*, pages 4803–4813. Association for Computational Linguistics.

Jun Zhao, Tao Gui, Qi Zhang, and Yaqian Zhou. 2021. A relation-oriented clustering method for open relation extraction. In *Proceedings of the 2021 Conference on Empirical Methods in Natural Language Processing*, pages 9707–9718.

Rui Zheng, Bao Rong, Yuhao Zhou, Di Liang, Sirui Wang, Wei Wu, Tao Gui, Qi Zhang, and Xuanjing Huang. 2022. Robust lottery tickets for pre-trained language models. In *Proceedings of the 60th Annual Meeting of the Association for Computational Linguistics (Volume 1: Long Papers), ACL 2022, Dublin, Ireland, May 22-27, 2022*, pages 2211–2224. Association for Computational Linguistics.

Jie Zhou, Xu Han, Cheng Yang, Zhiyuan Liu, Lifeng Wang, Changcheng Li, and Maosong Sun. 2019. GEAR: Graph-based evidence aggregating and reasoning for fact verification. In *Proceedings of the 57th Annual Meeting of the Association for Computational Linguistics*, pages 892–901, Florence, Italy. Association for Computational Linguistics.

Xin Zhou, Ruotian Ma, Tao Gui, Yiding Tan, Qi Zhang, and Xuanjing Huang. 2021. Plug-tagger: A pluggable sequence labeling framework using language models. *arXiv preprint arXiv:2110.07331*.

Wei Zhu. 2021. Autorc: Improving BERT based relation classification models via architecture search. In *Proceedings of the ACL-IJCNLP 2021 Student Research Workshop, ACL 2021, Online, JUli 5-10, 2021*, pages 33–43. Association for Computational Linguistics.

Recent Advances in Pre-trained Language Models: Why Do They Work and How Do They Work

Cheng-Han Chiang
National Taiwan University
dcml0714@gmail.com

Yung-Sung Chuang
CSAIL, MIT
yungsung@mit.edu

Hung-yi Lee
National Taiwan University
hungyilee@ntu.edu.tw

1 Brief Description

Deep learning-based natural language processing (NLP) has become mainstream research in recent years and has shown significant improvements over conventional methods. Among all deep learning methods, fine-tuning a self-supervisedly pre-trained language model (PLM) on downstream tasks of interest has become the standard pipeline in NLP tasks. Ever since ELMo (Peters et al., 2018) and BERT (Devlin et al., 2019) were proposed in 2018, models fine-tuned from PLMs have dominated numerous leader-boards in various tasks including question answering, natural language understanding, natural language inference, machine translation, and sentence similarity. Aside from applying PLMs on various downstream tasks, many have been delving into understanding the properties and characteristics of PLMs, including the linguistic knowledge encoded in the representations of PLMs, and the factual knowledge the PLMs acquire during pre-training. While it has been three years since PLMs were first proposed, there is no sign of decay in the research related to PLMs.

There were two tutorials focusing self-supervised learning/PLMs: a tutorial in NAACL 2019 (Ruder et al., 2019) and one in AACL 2020[1]. However, given the ever-evolving nature of this realm, it is conceivable that there have been significant progress in the study of PLMs. Specifically, compared with PLMs back in 2019, when they are mostly held by tech giants and used in scientific research, the PLMs nowadays have become more widely adopted in various real-world scenarios by users with different hardware infrastructures and amount of data, and thus posing problems that have never arisen before. Substantial progress, including possible answers to the effectiveness of PLMs and new training paradigms, have been made to allow PLMs better deployed in more realistic settings. Hence, we see it necessary and timely to inform the NLP community about the recent advances in PLMs through a well-organized tutorial.

This tutorial is divided into two parts: **why do PLMs work** and **how do PLMs work**. Table 1 summarizes the content this tutorial will cover. This tutorial intends to facilitate researchers in the NLP community to have a more comprehensive view of the advances in PLMs during recent years, and apply these newly emerging techniques to their domain of interest. As self-supervised learning and PLMs are very popular in these days, we expect our tutorial to have at least **100 attendees**.

Type of the tutorial The type of this tutorial is **Cutting-edge**. We will cover the cutting-edge advances in PLMs which have been flourishing in the NLP community **since 2020**. No tutorial has systematically reviewed any topics that we aim to cover (as listed in Table 1) at ACL/EMNLP/NAACL/EACL/AACL/COLING.

2 Tutorial Structure and Content

Pre-trained language models are language models that are pre-trained on large-scaled corpora in a self-supervised fashion. Traditional self-supervised pre-training tasks mostly involve recovering a corrupted input sentence, or auto-regressive language modeling. After these PLMs are pre-trained, they can be fine-tuned on downstream tasks. Conventionally, these fine-tuning protocol includes adding a linear layer on top of the PLMs and training the whole model on the downstream tasks, or formulating the downstream tasks as a sentence completion task and fine-tuning the downstream tasks in a seq2seq way. Fine-tuning PLMs on downstream tasks often yield exceptional performance gain, which is why PLMs have become so popular.

In the first part of the tutorial (**estimated 40**

[1] https://www.youtube.com/watch?v=0kgeff7PN14

Proceedings of the 2nd Conference of the Asia-Pacific Chapter of the Association for Computational Linguistics and the 12th International Joint Conference on Natural Language Processing: Tutorial Abstracts, pages 8–15
November 20-21, 2022. ©2022 Association for Computational Linguistics

Part	Sub-Category		References
(I) Why	(A) Empirical		Sinha et al. (2021); Aghajanyan et al. (2021); Chiang and Lee (2022); Sanh et al. (2022); Abdou et al. (2022)
	(B) Theoretical		Saunshi et al. (2020); Zhang and Hashimoto (2021); Lee et al. (2021); Xie et al. (2022)
(II) How	Pre-training	(C) Improving existing methods	Micheli et al. (2020); Zhang et al. (2021); Chiang et al. (2020); Izsak et al. (2021); Tay et al. (2022); Wettig et al. (2022); Gao et al. (2022); Hou et al. (2022)
		(D) New methods	Meng et al. (2021); Gao et al. (2021b); Su et al. (2021); Meng et al. (2022); Giorgi et al. (2021); Yan et al. (2021); Chuang et al. (2022); Du et al. (2022); Jiang et al. (2022); Jiang and Wang (2022); Zhang et al. (2022); Jian et al. (2022)
	Fine-tuning	(E) Parameter-efficient fine-tuning	**Adapter/Prefix tuning** Houlsby et al. (2019); Lester et al. (2021); Zhong et al. (2021); Qin and Eisner (2021); Zaken et al. (2021); Li and Liang (2021); Hambardzumyan et al. (2021); Hu et al. (2022); Mahabadi et al. (2021); He et al. (2022); Webson and Pavlick (2022)
		(F) Data-efficient fine-tuning	**Semi-supervised learning** Schick and Schütze (2021a,b); Mi et al. (2021); Lang et al. (2022) **Few-shot learning** Brown et al. (2020); Zhao et al. (2021); Gao et al. (2021a); Vu et al. (2021); Le Scao and Rush (2021); Min et al. (2022b); Cui et al. (2022); Min et al. (2022a); Zheng et al. (2022) **Zero-shot learning** Brown et al. (2020); Sanh et al. (2022); Wei et al. (2022); Xu et al. (2022); Aghajanyan et al. (2022)
		(G) Cross-task transfer	**Inter-mediate task fine-tuning**: Wang et al. (2019); Pruksachatkun et al. (2020); Vu et al. (2020); Phang et al. (2020); Chang and Lu (2021); Vu et al. (2022) **Multi-task learning**: Pilault et al. (2020); Chen et al. (2022)

Table 1: Works in the past three years (from 2020 to 2022) related to our tutorial, to list just a few.

mins), we will summarize some findings that partially explain why PLMs lead to exceptional downstream performance. Some of these results have helped researchers to design better pre-training and fine-tuning methods. In the second part (**estimated 2 hrs 20 mins**), we will introduce recent progress in how to pre-train and fine-tune PLMs; the new techniques covered in this part have been shown to bring significant efficiency in terms of hardware resource, training data, and model parameters while achieving superb performance.

2.1 Part I: Why Do PLMs Work

We will introduce several results that partially explain the effectiveness of PLMs from two aspects: empirical and theoretical.

2.1.1 Empirical Explanations

Many researchers have conducted empirical experiments to show what PLMs have learned during pre-training that aids downstream performance. They mostly construct a special pre-training dataset to examine the transferability of the PLM and draw connect the transferability of the PLM with the characteristic of the pre-training dataset. Block (A) in Table 1 lists the relevant works in recent years.

2.1.2 Theoretical Explanations

Some researchers aim to understand the effectiveness of PLMs by rigorous mathematics, as shown in block (B) in Table 1. Their results range from using statistical models to what PLMs are learning during pre-training, or bounding the generalization errors of the downstream tasks.

2.2 Part II: How Do PLM Work

In this part, we will introduce some new techniques in pre-training and fine-tuning PLMs.

2.2.1 Pre-training

Improving Existing Pre-training Methods Language model pre-training is a resource-hungry task when PLMs were first proposed, requiring a large amount of data, high-end hardware equipment, and lengthy pre-training time. To mitigate the above issues, some research aims to mitigate the above issues, as listed in block (C) in Table 1. Some of these works provide answers about the sufficient amount of data and time to pre-train a PLM that is good enough for downstream tasks, and others provide implementation optimization solutions to cut down the high-end requirement on hardware resources.

New Pre-training Methods Aside from improving existing pre-training methods, there have also been new pre-training methods designed for specific downstream tasks. One of the important topics we aim to cover is applying contrastive learning on language model pre-training. Contrastive learning has been widely applied to pre-training models in computer vision, and we will introduce how contrastive learning has improved PLMs recently. Relevant works are listed in block (D) in Table 1.

2.2.2 Fine-tuning

In this part, we will go through several important fine-tuning protocols that have emerged recently. We categorize them based on the scenario in which the fine-tuning method is used.

Parameter-Efficient Fine-tuning PLMs are enormous, often having millions or even billions of numbers of parameters. In the traditional fine-tuning method, fine-tuning each distinct downstream task produces a fine-tuned model that is are bulky as the original PLM. To reduce the number of parameters for fine-tuning PLMs on downstream tasks, there has been a surge of research on parameter-efficient fine-tuning in NLP, as listed in block (E) in Table 1.

Data-Efficient Fine-tuning A large amount of labeled data is not always available for all downstream tasks, and it is thus important to find a way to apply the PLMs on downstream tasks with limited labeled data. These endeavors are included in block (F) in Table 1. We will discuss how to apply PLMs under different levels of labeled data scarcity.

In case we have a large amount of unlabeled data, **semi-supervised learning** fine-tuning protocols provide effective ways to utilize those unlabeled data and can boost the downstream performance. If those few labeled data are the only thing available, then we must harness the knowledge that the PLM possesses to aid the performance of **few-shot learning**. When we have no labeled data, **zero-shot learning** is still possible in certain cases, if you use the PLM correctly. We will discuss how to make a PLM able to perform well in the zero-shot setting.

Cross-Task Transfer When we have a target task of interest, it is canonical to fine-tune the PLM on the target task. While transferring from PLMs leads to exceptional performance gain, sometimes we want more. This can be achieved by transferring from the PLMs *and* additional guidance from other auxiliary tasks in the form of **intermediate task fine-tuning** or **mutitask learning**. Relevant works are listed in block (G) in Table 1. We will discuss how can cross-task transfer improve the downstream performance together with the power of PLMs.

3 Diversity

PLMs have shown promising results on different domains and have boosted the performance of low-resource languages on many tasks. The **why part** covered in this tutorial has the potential to help individuals of different groups to pre-train their own PLMs more efficiently. The **how part** covered in this tutorial specifically focuses on how to apply PLMs under different real-world scenarios with data scarcity and restricted model parameters, which will enable individuals of different groups to apply PLMs on the domains of interest in a more realistic setting. We see this tutorial to benefit diverse groups in the community.

The tutorial instructors are also diverse: Chuang is a PhD student in the USA, and Lee and Chiang are researchers in Taiwan. Also, Chuang and Chiang are currently Ph.D. students familiar with precise implementations, while Lee is a senior researcher with ten years of experience in human language processing research. This diversity in members enables our team to provide a thorough and detailed yet comprehensive and unified view on PLMs.

4 Prerequisites for Attendees

We expect the attendees to have basic machine learning concepts such as gradient descent and model optimization. The attendees will need to have basic knowledge in linear algebra and calculus to understand some contents in block (B) in Table 1. The attendees should also have minimal knowledge about PLMs and transformer models.

5 Reading List

We encourage attendees to read the following emblematic papers on PLMs and transformer model architectures:

- Transformer model: Vaswani et al. (2017)
- PLMs: Radford et al.; Devlin et al. (2019); Raffel et al. (2019)

6 Biographies of Presenters

Cheng-Han Chiang[2] is a PhD student in National Taiwan University. His research focuses on natural language processing and self-supervised learning, and he has published several papers analyzing PLMs. He has experiences in giving lectures on machine learning topics: he gave a lecture on BERT in AI Summer School 2020[3], and his two lectures on graph neural network (in Mandarin) has received over **68k** views on Youtube [4][5]. He has also served as reviewers in EMNLP 2021, ICLR 2022, NeurIPS 2022, EMNLP 2022, and AAAI 2023.

Yung-Sung Chuang[6] is a PhD student in Electrical Engineering and Computer Science at MIT CSAIL, where he works with Dr. James Glass. His research focuses on learning representations for natural language which helps downstream tasks such as natural language understanding, natural language generation, question answering. He has published several paper in this direction in EMNLP, ACL, NeurIPS, and NAACL. He also has served as reviewers in NeurIPS 2021, ICLR 2022, ICML 2022, NeurIPS 2022, EMNLP 2022, and AAAI 2023.

Hung-yi Lee[7] is an associate professor of the Department of Electrical Engineering of National Taiwan University, with a joint appointment at the Department of Computer Science & Information Engineering of the university. His research focuses on deep learning, speech processing, and natural language processing. He owns a YouTube channel teaching deep learning (in Mandarin) with more than **8M** views and **100k** subscribers. He gave tutorials at ICASSP 2018[8], APSIPA 2018, ISCSLP 2018, INTERSPEECH 2019[9], SIPS 2019, INTERSPEECH 2020, ICASSP 2021, ACL 2021. He is the co-organizer of the special session on "New Trends in self-supervised speech processing" at INTERSPEECH (2020), the workshop on "Self-Supervised Learning for Speech and Audio Processing" at NeurIPS (2020), the workshop on "Meta Learning and Its Applications to Natural Language Processing" at ACL (2021), and the workshop on "Self-Supervised Learning for Speech and Audio Processing" at AAAI (2022). He will give the tutorial, "Self-supervised Representation

[2] https://d223302.github.io/

[3] https://ai.ntu.edu.tw/?p=3534

[4] https://www.youtube.com/watch?v=eybCCtNKwzA&ab_channel=Hung-yiLee

[5] https://www.youtube.com/watch?v=M9ht8vsVEw8&ab_channel=Hung-yiLee

[6] https://people.csail.mit.edu/yungsung/

[7] https://speech.ee.ntu.edu.tw/~hylee/index.php

[8] The tutorial has the most participants among the 14 tutorials in ICASSP 2018.

[9] The tutorial also has the most participants among the 8 tutorials in INTERSPEECH 2019.

Learning for Speech Processing" with other researchers at ICASSP 2022 and NAACL 2022. He is the lead guest editor of IEEE JSTSP Special Issue on Self-Supervised Learning for Speech and Audio Processing, member of the Speech and Language Technical Committee (SLTC) of IEEE Signal Processing Society (SPS), SPS Education Center Editorial Board member, and Associate Editor for the SPS Open Journal of Signal Processing.

7 Open Access

We will allow our slides and video recording of the tutorial published in the ACL Anthology. All the slides and videos used in the tutorial, along with the reading lists related with the tutorial, will be updated at this tutorial website[10].

References

Mostafa Abdou, Vinit Ravishankar, Artur Kulmizev, and Anders Søgaard. 2022. Word order does matter and shuffled language models know it. In *Proceedings of the 60th Annual Meeting of the Association for Computational Linguistics (Volume 1: Long Papers)*, pages 6907–6919, Dublin, Ireland. Association for Computational Linguistics.

Armen Aghajanyan, Sonal Gupta, and Luke Zettlemoyer. 2021. Intrinsic dimensionality explains the effectiveness of language model fine-tuning. In *Proceedings of the 59th Annual Meeting of the Association for Computational Linguistics and the 11th International Joint Conference on Natural Language Processing (Volume 1: Long Papers)*, pages 7319–7328.

Armen Aghajanyan, Dmytro Okhonko, Mike Lewis, Mandar Joshi, Hu Xu, Gargi Ghosh, and Luke Zettlemoyer. 2022. Htlm: Hyper-text pre-training and prompting of language models.

Tom Brown, Benjamin Mann, Nick Ryder, Melanie Subbiah, Jared D Kaplan, Prafulla Dhariwal, Arvind Neelakantan, Pranav Shyam, Girish Sastry, Amanda Askell, et al. 2020. Language models are few-shot learners. *Advances in neural information processing systems*, 33:1877–1901.

Ting-Yun Chang and Chi-Jen Lu. 2021. Rethinking why intermediate-task fine-tuning works. In *Findings of the Association for Computational Linguistics: EMNLP 2021*, pages 706–713, Punta Cana, Dominican Republic. Association for Computational Linguistics.

Shuxiao Chen, Koby Crammer, Hangfeng He, Dan Roth, and Weijie J Su. 2022. Weighted training for cross-task learning.

[10] `https://d223302.github.io/AACL2022-Pretrain-Language-Model-Tutorial/`

Cheng-Han Chiang, Sung-Feng Huang, and Hung-yi Lee. 2020. Pretrained language model embryology: The birth of ALBERT. In *Proceedings of the 2020 Conference on Empirical Methods in Natural Language Processing (EMNLP)*, pages 6813–6828, Online. Association for Computational Linguistics.

Cheng-Han Chiang and Hung-yi Lee. 2022. On the transferability of pre-trained language models: A study from artificial datasets. In *Proceedings of the AAAI Conference on Artificial Intelligence*.

Yung-Sung Chuang, Rumen Dangovski, Hongyin Luo, Yang Zhang, Shiyu Chang, Marin Soljacic, Shang-Wen Li, Scott Yih, Yoon Kim, and James Glass. 2022. DiffCSE: Difference-based contrastive learning for sentence embeddings. In *Proceedings of the 2022 Conference of the North American Chapter of the Association for Computational Linguistics: Human Language Technologies*, pages 4207–4218, Seattle, United States. Association for Computational Linguistics.

Ganqu Cui, Shengding Hu, Ning Ding, Longtao Huang, and Zhiyuan Liu. 2022. Prototypical verbalizer for prompt-based few-shot tuning. In *Proceedings of the 60th Annual Meeting of the Association for Computational Linguistics (Volume 1: Long Papers)*, pages 7014–7024, Dublin, Ireland. Association for Computational Linguistics.

Jacob Devlin, Ming-Wei Chang, Kenton Lee, and Kristina Toutanova. 2019. BERT: Pre-training of deep bidirectional transformers for language understanding. In *Proceedings of the 2019 Conference of the North American Chapter of the Association for Computational Linguistics: Human Language Technologies, Volume 1 (Long and Short Papers)*, pages 4171–4186, Minneapolis, Minnesota. Association for Computational Linguistics.

Zhengxiao Du, Yujie Qian, Xiao Liu, Ming Ding, Jiezhong Qiu, Zhilin Yang, and Jie Tang. 2022. GLM: General language model pretraining with autoregressive blank infilling. In *Proceedings of the 60th Annual Meeting of the Association for Computational Linguistics (Volume 1: Long Papers)*, pages 320–335, Dublin, Ireland. Association for Computational Linguistics.

Jiahui Gao, Hang Xu, Xiaozhe Ren, Philip LH Yu, Xiaodan Liang, Xin Jiang, Zhenguo Li, et al. 2022. Autobert-zero: Evolving bert backbone from scratch. In *Proceedings of the AAAI Conference on Artificial Intelligence*.

Tianyu Gao, Adam Fisch, and Danqi Chen. 2021a. Making pre-trained language models better few-shot learners. In *Proceedings of the 59th Annual Meeting of the Association for Computational Linguistics and the 11th International Joint Conference on Natural Language Processing (Volume 1: Long Papers)*, pages 3816–3830, Online. Association for Computational Linguistics.

Tianyu Gao, Xingcheng Yao, and Danqi Chen. 2021b. Simcse: Simple contrastive learning of sentence embeddings. In *Proceedings of the 2021 Conference on Empirical Methods in Natural Language Processing*, pages 6894–6910.

John Giorgi, Osvald Nitski, Bo Wang, and Gary Bader. 2021. Declutr: Deep contrastive learning for unsupervised textual representations. In *Proceedings of the 59th Annual Meeting of the Association for Computational Linguistics and the 11th International Joint Conference on Natural Language Processing (Volume 1: Long Papers)*, pages 879–895.

Karen Hambardzumyan, Hrant Khachatrian, and Jonathan May. 2021. WARP: Word-level Adversarial ReProgramming. In *Proceedings of the 59th Annual Meeting of the Association for Computational Linguistics and the 11th International Joint Conference on Natural Language Processing (Volume 1: Long Papers)*, pages 4921–4933, Online. Association for Computational Linguistics.

Junxian He, Chunting Zhou, Xuezhe Ma, Taylor Berg-Kirkpatrick, and Graham Neubig. 2022. Towards a unified view of parameter-efficient transfer learning.

Le Hou, Richard Yuanzhe Pang, Tianyi Zhou, Yuexin Wu, Xinying Song, Xiaodan Song, and Denny Zhou. 2022. Token dropping for efficient BERT pretraining. In *Proceedings of the 60th Annual Meeting of the Association for Computational Linguistics (Volume 1: Long Papers)*, pages 3774–3784, Dublin, Ireland. Association for Computational Linguistics.

Neil Houlsby, Andrei Giurgiu, Stanislaw Jastrzebski, Bruna Morrone, Quentin De Laroussilhe, Andrea Gesmundo, Mona Attariyan, and Sylvain Gelly. 2019. Parameter-efficient transfer learning for nlp. In *International Conference on Machine Learning*, pages 2790–2799. PMLR.

Edward J Hu, Yelong Shen, Phillip Wallis, Zeyuan Allen-Zhu, Yuanzhi Li, Shean Wang, Lu Wang, and Weizhu Chen. 2022. Lora: Low-rank adaptation of large language models.

Peter Izsak, Moshe Berchansky, and Omer Levy. 2021. How to train BERT with an academic budget. In *Proceedings of the 2021 Conference on Empirical Methods in Natural Language Processing*, pages 10644–10652, Online and Punta Cana, Dominican Republic. Association for Computational Linguistics.

Yiren Jian, Chongyang Gao, and Soroush Vosoughi. 2022. Non-linguistic supervision for contrastive learning of sentence embeddings. *arXiv preprint arXiv:2209.09433*.

Ting Jiang, Shaohan Huang, Zihan Zhang, Deqing Wang, Fuzhen Zhuang, Furu Wei, Haizhen Huang, Liangjie Zhang, and Qi Zhang. 2022. Promptbert: Improving bert sentence embeddings with prompts. *arXiv preprint arXiv:2201.04337*.

Yuxin Jiang and Wei Wang. 2022. Deep continuous prompt for contrastive learning of sentence embeddings. *arXiv preprint arXiv:2203.06875*.

Hunter Lang, Monica Agrawal, Yoon Kim, and David Sontag. 2022. Co-training improves prompt-based learning for large language models. *arXiv preprint arXiv:2202.00828*.

Teven Le Scao and Alexander Rush. 2021. How many data points is a prompt worth? In *Proceedings of the 2021 Conference of the North American Chapter of the Association for Computational Linguistics: Human Language Technologies*, pages 2627–2636, Online. Association for Computational Linguistics.

Jason D Lee, Qi Lei, Nikunj Saunshi, and Jiacheng Zhuo. 2021. Predicting what you already know helps: Provable self-supervised learning. *Advances in Neural Information Processing Systems*, 34.

Brian Lester, Rami Al-Rfou, and Noah Constant. 2021. The power of scale for parameter-efficient prompt tuning. In *Proceedings of the 2021 Conference on Empirical Methods in Natural Language Processing*, pages 3045–3059, Online and Punta Cana, Dominican Republic. Association for Computational Linguistics.

Xiang Lisa Li and Percy Liang. 2021. Prefix-tuning: Optimizing continuous prompts for generation. In *Proceedings of the 59th Annual Meeting of the Association for Computational Linguistics and the 11th International Joint Conference on Natural Language Processing (Volume 1: Long Papers)*, pages 4582–4597, Online. Association for Computational Linguistics.

Rabeeh Karimi Mahabadi, Sebastian Ruder, Mostafa Dehghani, and James Henderson. 2021. Parameter-efficient multi-task fine-tuning for transformers via shared hypernetworks. In *Proceedings of the 59th Annual Meeting of the Association for Computational Linguistics and the 11th International Joint Conference on Natural Language Processing (Volume 1: Long Papers)*, pages 565–576.

Yu Meng, Chenyan Xiong, Payal Bajaj, Paul Bennett, Jiawei Han, Xia Song, et al. 2021. Coco-lm: Correcting and contrasting text sequences for language model pretraining. *Advances in Neural Information Processing Systems*, 34.

Yu Meng, Chenyan Xiong, Payal Bajaj, Paul N Bennett, Jiawei Han, Xia Song, et al. 2022. Pretraining text encoders with adversarial mixture of training signal generators. In *International Conference on Learning Representations*.

Fei Mi, Wanhao Zhou, Lingjing Kong, Fengyu Cai, Minlie Huang, and Boi Faltings. 2021. Self-training improves pre-training for few-shot learning in task-oriented dialog systems. In *Proceedings of the 2021 Conference on Empirical Methods in Natural Language Processing*, pages 1887–1898, Online and

Punta Cana, Dominican Republic. Association for Computational Linguistics.

Vincent Micheli, Martin d'Hoffschmidt, and François Fleuret. 2020. On the importance of pre-training data volume for compact language models. In *Proceedings of the 2020 Conference on Empirical Methods in Natural Language Processing (EMNLP)*, pages 7853–7858.

Sewon Min, Mike Lewis, Hannaneh Hajishirzi, and Luke Zettlemoyer. 2022a. Noisy channel language model prompting for few-shot text classification. In *Proceedings of the 60th Annual Meeting of the Association for Computational Linguistics (Volume 1: Long Papers)*, pages 5316–5330, Dublin, Ireland. Association for Computational Linguistics.

Sewon Min, Xinxi Lyu, Ari Holtzman, Mikel Artetxe, Mike Lewis, Hannaneh Hajishirzi, and Luke Zettlemoyer. 2022b. Rethinking the role of demonstrations: What makes in-context learning work? *arXiv preprint arXiv:2202.12837*.

Matthew E. Peters, Mark Neumann, Mohit Iyyer, Matt Gardner, Christopher Clark, Kenton Lee, and Luke Zettlemoyer. 2018. Deep contextualized word representations. In *Proceedings of the 2018 Conference of the North American Chapter of the Association for Computational Linguistics: Human Language Technologies, Volume 1 (Long Papers)*, pages 2227–2237, New Orleans, Louisiana. Association for Computational Linguistics.

Jason Phang, Iacer Calixto, Phu Mon Htut, Yada Pruksachatkun, Haokun Liu, Clara Vania, Katharina Kann, and Samuel Bowman. 2020. English intermediate-task training improves zero-shot cross-lingual transfer too. In *Proceedings of the 1st Conference of the Asia-Pacific Chapter of the Association for Computational Linguistics and the 10th International Joint Conference on Natural Language Processing*, pages 557–575.

Jonathan Pilault, Christopher Pal, et al. 2020. Conditionally adaptive multi-task learning: Improving transfer learning in nlp using fewer parameters & less data. In *International Conference on Learning Representations*.

Yada Pruksachatkun, Jason Phang, Haokun Liu, Phu Mon Htut, Xiaoyi Zhang, Richard Yuanzhe Pang, Clara Vania, Katharina Kann, and Samuel Bowman. 2020. Intermediate-task transfer learning with pretrained language models: When and why does it work? In *Proceedings of the 58th Annual Meeting of the Association for Computational Linguistics*, pages 5231–5247.

Guanghui Qin and Jason Eisner. 2021. Learning how to ask: Querying LMs with mixtures of soft prompts. In *Proceedings of the 2021 Conference of the North American Chapter of the Association for Computational Linguistics: Human Language Technologies*, pages 5203–5212, Online. Association for Computational Linguistics.

Alec Radford, Karthik Narasimhan, Tim Salimans, and Ilya Sutskever. Improving language understanding by generative pre-training.

Colin Raffel, Noam Shazeer, Adam Roberts, Katherine Lee, Sharan Narang, Michael Matena, Yanqi Zhou, Wei Li, and Peter J Liu. 2019. Exploring the limits of transfer learning with a unified text-to-text transformer. *arXiv preprint arXiv:1910.10683*.

Sebastian Ruder, Matthew E. Peters, Swabha Swayamdipta, and Thomas Wolf. 2019. Transfer learning in natural language processing. In *Proceedings of the 2019 Conference of the North American Chapter of the Association for Computational Linguistics: Tutorials*, pages 15–18, Minneapolis, Minnesota. Association for Computational Linguistics.

Victor Sanh, Albert Webson, Colin Raffel, Stephen H Bach, Lintang Sutawika, Zaid Alyafeai, Antoine Chaffin, Arnaud Stiegler, Teven Le Scao, Arun Raja, et al. 2022. Multitask prompted training enables zero-shot task generalization.

Nikunj Saunshi, Sadhika Malladi, and Sanjeev Arora. 2020. A mathematical exploration of why language models help solve downstream tasks. In *International Conference on Learning Representations*.

Timo Schick and Hinrich Schütze. 2021a. Exploiting cloze-questions for few-shot text classification and natural language inference. In *Proceedings of the 16th Conference of the European Chapter of the Association for Computational Linguistics: Main Volume*, pages 255–269, Online. Association for Computational Linguistics.

Timo Schick and Hinrich Schütze. 2021b. It's not just size that matters: Small language models are also few-shot learners. In *Proceedings of the 2021 Conference of the North American Chapter of the Association for Computational Linguistics: Human Language Technologies*, pages 2339–2352, Online. Association for Computational Linguistics.

Koustuv Sinha, Robin Jia, Dieuwke Hupkes, Joelle Pineau, Adina Williams, and Douwe Kiela. 2021. Masked language modeling and the distributional hypothesis: Order word matters pre-training for little. In *Proceedings of the 2021 Conference on Empirical Methods in Natural Language Processing*, pages 2888–2913.

Yixuan Su, Fangyu Liu, Zaiqiao Meng, Lei Shu, Ehsan Shareghi, and Nigel Collier. 2021. Tacl: Improving bert pre-training with token-aware contrastive learning. *arXiv preprint arXiv:2111.04198*.

Yi Tay, Mostafa Dehghani, Jinfeng Rao, William Fedus, Samira Abnar, Hyung Won Chung, Sharan Narang, Dani Yogatama, Ashish Vaswani, and Donald Metzler. 2022. Scale efficiently: Insights from pre-training and fine-tuning transformers. In *International Conference on Learning Representations*.

Ashish Vaswani, Noam Shazeer, Niki Parmar, Jakob Uszkoreit, Llion Jones, Aidan N Gomez, Łukasz Kaiser, and Illia Polosukhin. 2017. Attention is all you need. *Advances in neural information processing systems*, 30.

Tu Vu, Brian Lester, Noah Constant, Rami Al-Rfou', and Daniel Cer. 2022. SPoT: Better frozen model adaptation through soft prompt transfer. In *Proceedings of the 60th Annual Meeting of the Association for Computational Linguistics (Volume 1: Long Papers)*, pages 5039–5059, Dublin, Ireland. Association for Computational Linguistics.

Tu Vu, Minh-Thang Luong, Quoc Le, Grady Simon, and Mohit Iyyer. 2021. STraTA: Self-training with task augmentation for better few-shot learning. In *Proceedings of the 2021 Conference on Empirical Methods in Natural Language Processing*, pages 5715–5731, Online and Punta Cana, Dominican Republic. Association for Computational Linguistics.

Tu Vu, Tong Wang, Tsendsuren Munkhdalai, Alessandro Sordoni, Adam Trischler, Andrew Mattarella-Micke, Subhransu Maji, and Mohit Iyyer. 2020. Exploring and predicting transferability across NLP tasks. In *Proceedings of the 2020 Conference on Empirical Methods in Natural Language Processing (EMNLP)*, pages 7882–7926, Online. Association for Computational Linguistics.

Alex Wang, Jan Hula, Patrick Xia, Raghavendra Pappagari, R Thomas McCoy, Roma Patel, Najoung Kim, Ian Tenney, Yinghui Huang, Katherin Yu, et al. 2019. Can you tell me how to get past sesame street? sentence-level pretraining beyond language modeling. In *Proceedings of the 57th Annual Meeting of the Association for Computational Linguistics*, pages 4465–4476.

Albert Webson and Ellie Pavlick. 2022. Do prompt-based models really understand the meaning of their prompts? In *Proceedings of the 2022 Conference of the North American Chapter of the Association for Computational Linguistics: Human Language Technologies*, pages 2300–2344, Seattle, United States. Association for Computational Linguistics.

Jason Wei, Maarten Bosma, Vincent Y Zhao, Kelvin Guu, Adams Wei Yu, Brian Lester, Nan Du, Andrew M Dai, and Quoc V Le. 2022. Finetuned language models are zero-shot learners.

Alexander Wettig, Tianyu Gao, Zexuan Zhong, and Danqi Chen. 2022. Should you mask 15% in masked language modeling? *arXiv preprint arXiv:2202.08005*.

Sang Michael Xie, Aditi Raghunathan, Percy Liang, and Tengyu Ma. 2022. An explanation of in-context learning as implicit bayesian inference.

Hanwei Xu, Yujun Chen, Yulun Du, Nan Shao, Yanggang Wang, Haiyu Li, and Zhilin Yang. 2022. Zero-prompt: Scaling prompt-based pretraining to 1,000 tasks improves zero-shot generalization. *arXiv preprint arXiv:2201.06910*.

Yuanmeng Yan, Rumei Li, Sirui Wang, Fuzheng Zhang, Wei Wu, and Weiran Xu. 2021. Consert: A contrastive framework for self-supervised sentence representation transfer. In *Proceedings of the 59th Annual Meeting of the Association for Computational Linguistics and the 11th International Joint Conference on Natural Language Processing (Volume 1: Long Papers)*, pages 5065–5075.

Elad Ben Zaken, Shauli Ravfogel, and Yoav Goldberg. 2021. Bitfit: Simple parameter-efficient fine-tuning for transformer-based masked language-models. *arXiv preprint arXiv:2106.10199*.

Miaoran Zhang, Marius Mosbach, David Ifeoluwa Adelani, Michael A Hedderich, and Dietrich Klakow. 2022. Mcse: Multimodal contrastive learning of sentence embeddings. *arXiv preprint arXiv:2204.10931*.

Tianyi Zhang and Tatsunori B Hashimoto. 2021. On the inductive bias of masked language modeling: From statistical to syntactic dependencies. In *Proceedings of the 2021 Conference of the North American Chapter of the Association for Computational Linguistics: Human Language Technologies*, pages 5131–5146.

Yian Zhang, Alex Warstadt, Xiaocheng Li, and Samuel R. Bowman. 2021. When do you need billions of words of pretraining data? In *Proceedings of the 59th Annual Meeting of the Association for Computational Linguistics and the 11th International Joint Conference on Natural Language Processing (Volume 1: Long Papers)*, pages 1112–1125, Online. Association for Computational Linguistics.

Zihao Zhao, Eric Wallace, Shi Feng, Dan Klein, and Sameer Singh. 2021. Calibrate before use: Improving few-shot performance of language models. In *International Conference on Machine Learning*, pages 12697–12706. PMLR.

Yanan Zheng, Jing Zhou, Yujie Qian, Ming Ding, Chonghua Liao, Li Jian, Ruslan Salakhutdinov, Jie Tang, Sebastian Ruder, and Zhilin Yang. 2022. FewNLU: Benchmarking state-of-the-art methods for few-shot natural language understanding. In *Proceedings of the 60th Annual Meeting of the Association for Computational Linguistics (Volume 1: Long Papers)*, pages 501–516, Dublin, Ireland. Association for Computational Linguistics.

Zexuan Zhong, Dan Friedman, and Danqi Chen. 2021. Factual probing is [MASK]: Learning vs. learning to recall. In *Proceedings of the 2021 Conference of the North American Chapter of the Association for Computational Linguistics: Human Language Technologies*, pages 5017–5033, Online. Association for Computational Linguistics.

When Cantonese NLP Meets Pre-training: Progress and Challenges

Rong Xiang[1] **Hanzhuo Tan**[1] **Jing Li**[1] **Mingyu Wan**[2] **Kam-Fai Wong**[3]
[1] Department of Computing, Hong Kong Polytechnic University, HKSAR, China
[2] School of Continuing Education, Hong Kong Baptist University, HKSAR, China
[3] Department of SEEM, The Chinese University of Hong Kong, HKSAR, China
[1]{rong.xiang, hanzhuo.tan}@connect.polyu.hk
[1]jing-amelia.li@polyu.edu.hk [2]claramywan629@hkbu.edu.hk
[3]kfwong@se.cuhk.edu.hk

Abstract

Cantonese is an influential Chinese variant with a large population of speakers worldwide. However, it is under-resourced in terms of the data scale and diversity, excluding Cantonese Natural Language Processing (NLP) from the state-of-the-art (SOTA) "pre-training and fine-tuning" paradigm. This tutorial will start with a substantially review of the linguistics and NLP progress for shaping language specificity, resources, and methodologies. It will be followed by an introduction to the trendy transformer-based pre-training methods, which have been largely advancing the SOTA performance of a wide range of downstream NLP tasks in numerous majority languages (e.g., English and Chinese). Based on the above, we will present the main challenges for Cantonese NLP in relation to Cantonese language idiosyncrasies of *colloquialism* and *multilingualism*, followed by the future directions to line NLP for Cantonese and other low-resource languages up to the cutting-edge pre-training practice.

1 Tutorial Description

In our tutorial, there will be five parts (shown in Figure 1), each presented by a tutorial presenter. The first part will be the overview of Cantonese NLP research (PART I) and the second exhibits the progress in language specify, resources, and methodologies (PART II). Then, we will introduce the roles played by language pre-training in the SOTA NLP practice (PART III), based on which we further discuss the challenges to benefit Cantonese NLP from the trendy "pre-training and fine-tuning" fashion (PART IV). Lastly, the potential solutions will be pointed out to shed light on the promising future direction of Cantonese NLP (PART V).

The detailed content is shown in the following.

PART I: Cantonese NLP Overview (in 30 min). At the beginning, we will briefly introduce Cantonese language and its related research in NLP.

Cantonese is a language from the Chinese family with over 73 million speakers in the world (García and Fishman, 2011; Yu, 2013). It is mostly used in colloquial scenarios (e.g., daily conversation and social media) and exhibits different vocabulary, grammar, and pronunciation compared to standard Chinese (SCN)[1], which is mainly designed for formal writing (Wong and Lee, 2018).

Despite the substantial efforts in Chinese Natural Language Processing (NLP), most previous studies center around SCN, where limited work attempts to explore how to process Cantonese with the cutting-edge NLP techniques (Xiang et al., 2019; Lee et al., 2021). Modern NLP paradigms have been deeply revolutionized by large-scale pre-training models, e.g., BERT (Devlin et al., 2019) and GPT-3 (Brown et al., 2020), which have achieved SOTA performance on many NLP tasks via fine-tuning.

Although the general NLP field is thriving, Cantonese NLP has drawn limited attention so far, as demonstrated by the recent publications in the ACL Anthology — only 47 papers are related to "Cantonese", compared to 7,018 papers for English, 2,355 for common Chinese, and 323 for Mandarin.

This tutorial will present a roadmap lining Cantonese NLP up to the SOTA practice based on pre-training. We will start with the previous progress made by linguistics and NLP researchers, followed by the major challenges caused by the language specificity, and end with the promising future directions to allow Cantonese and other low resource languages to benefit from the advanced NLP techniques. The details will be covered in PART II-V.

PART II: Progress in Language Specificity, Resources, and Methodologies (in 40 min). Cantonese (or Yue) is the second most popular dialect among all Chinese variants (Matthews and Yip, 2011). For-

[1]Standard Chinese is known as Standard Northern Mandarin, which is emerged as the lingua franca among the speakers of various Mandarin and other varieties of Chinese (Hokkien, Cantonese, and beyond).

Proceedings of the 2nd Conference of the Asia-Pacific Chapter of the Association for Computational Linguistics and the 12th International Joint Conference on Natural Language Processing: Tutorial Abstracts, pages 16–21
November 20-21, 2022.

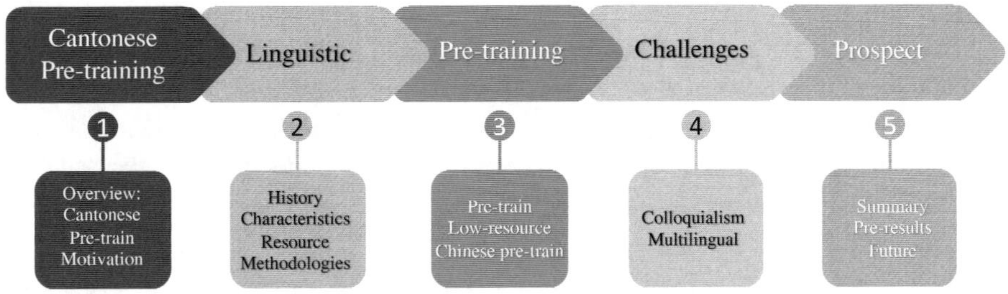

Figure 1: Outline for the tutorial

mal writing exhibits no essential difference among the SCN in various regions (Kataoka and Lee, 2008; Yu, 2013), whereas in informal situations, colloquial Cantonese diverges substantially from SCN in phonology, orthography, lexicon, and grammar.

In dealing with Cantonese data, *Colloquialism* and *Multilingualism* are two fundamental challenges. Unlike standard Chinese, which character standardization can be dated back to the Qin dynasty (221 BC), Cantonese is mainly derived from pronunciation and may contain many colloquial features, such as non-standard spelling, local slang, neologisms. On the other hand, Cantonese language historically evolved in multi-lingual environments and this is especially true for HK Cantonese, as shown by the large inventory of English loanwords borrowed through phonetic transliteration.

Unlike SCN, which benefits from abundant well-annotated textual resources, there is a chronic lack of digital resources for Cantonese data. The existing resources are summarized into three categories: *Corpora*, *Benchmarks*, and *Expert Resources*. In general, using existing Cantonese resources may be difficult for three reasons: (1) the data scale is relatively small (especially compared to SCN); (2) the domain is usually specific and lacks diversity and generality; (3) many resources mix Cantonese and SCN which might confuse NLP models and hinder them from mastering 'authentic' Cantonese.

Cantonese specific NLP methods are relatively less explored. The following presents a detailed review of Cantonese NLP methods in (1) Natural Language Understanding and (2) Natural Language Generation. Several language understanding tasks will be introduced, including word segmentation, spell checking, rumor detection, sentiment analysis, and dialogue slot filling. As for language generation, we will summarize previous studies on dialogue summarization, machine translation, etc.

PART III: Pre-training in SOTA NLP (in 40 min). The cutting-edge NLP takes advantages of the promising results achieved by the pre-training of language representations. A typical pre-trained and fine-tune scheme refers to pre-train a large model on massive unlabelled corpora by self-supervised objectives, and fine-tune the model on downstream tasks with task-specific loss. Such self-supervised objectives, e.g. Masked Langauge Modeling (MLM) and Next Sentene Prediction (NSP) (Devlin et al., 2019) enable the model to gain generalized language representations without human supervision. During fine-tuning stage, the pre-trained representations can be further used to learn a specific Natural Language Understanding (NLU) task with small-scale annotations via incremental training.

Transformer (Devlin et al., 2019; Liu et al., 2019; Brown et al., 2020) is the most widely employed pre-trained architecture in NLP. The transformer encoder consumes the input text and project it into high-dimension vectors, which are feed into the transformer decoder to generate the output sequences. Inspired by the transformer architecture, researchers explore the transformer encoder for NLU tasks and transformer decoder for Natural Language Generation (NLG) tasks.

Since the transformer-based pre-training (Devlin et al., 2019; Liu et al., 2019) was introduced to the world, championing the leaderboards of many NLP benchmarks, the "pre-training and fine-tuning" paradigm has profoundly revolutionized the way we research NLP for most of the majority languages, such as English and Chinese. Nevertheless, the success of language pre-training is built upon the availability of rich language resources and large-scale textual corpora, hindering Cantonese and other low-resource languages from gaining the benefit of pre-training. The following presents the challenging low-resource issue in Cantonese.

PART IV: Challenges from Colloquialism and

Multilingualism (40 min). In Cantonese NLP, *Colloquialism* and *Multilingualism* jointly present the low-resource challenges. Cantonese is by nature colloquial, where using casual language would sparsify the context and require more data for contextual model training, making the low-resource issue serious. Like other low-resource language processing (Li et al., 2018), it is possible to gather large-scale data from social media. However, models might also compromise their performance using just noisy social media data. It not only requires effective data cleaning and augmentation, but also non-trivial model capabilities of capturing salient information in context with diverse quality.

Cantonese exhibits a code-switching convention with multiple languages. Substantially richer context is hence required for NLP models to gain the multilingual understanding capabilities, despite the limitation to make it happen in the low-resource scenarios. Although it is possible to transfer the knowledge gained in a similar language with rich resources (henceforth *cross-lingual learning*) (Friedrich and Gateva, 2017; Khalil et al., 2019; Zhang et al., 2019), Cantonese, as a vibrant language, absorbs the knowledge from numerous languages beyond SCN and English.

PART V: Future NLP Directions for Cantonese and other Low-Resource Languages (30 min). Data scarcity and limited methodology exploration are top issues for Cantonese in benefiting deep semantics and general NLP tasks. To mitigate low-resource problems, data augmentation is an alternative to scale up the Cantonese dataset for NLP model training. For example, we might employ heuristic rules (Ratner et al., 2017; Lison et al., 2020), machine learning (Şahin and Steedman, 2018) and information retrieval (Riedel et al., 2010; Hedderich et al., 2021) to automatically boost the data scales. In the augmentation process, we might need to learn how to distinguish SCN from Cantonese. Though both are encoded in the Chinese language system, the former dominates the Chinese resources while the latter is a minority (Wu and Dredze, 2020; Cui et al., 2021).

Cross-lingual learning might provide another be a promising alternative for the pre-training in low resource, which borrows knowledge from other languages (Wisniewski et al., 2014; Zhang et al., 2019; Khalil et al., 2019). We may take advantage of SOTA pre-trained transformers to capture the general and specific language features for transfer learning (Devlin et al., 2019; Clark et al., 2020). In addition, based on Cantonese's phonological history, future work may consider injecting phonetic knowledge into language learning or developing multi-modal understanding across text and speech.

2 Type of the Tutorial

This is an *introductory* tutorial of *Cantonese NLP*, where we draw NLP community's attention to look at the research of Cantonese — a language with over 73 million speakers in the world (García and Fishman, 2011; Yu, 2013) while only has 47 papers in ACL Anthology related to it. The tutorial will present a roadmap going through the essential issues regarding language specificity, data scarcity, research progress, and major challenges for Cantonese NLP to be benefited from the cutting-edge NLP paradigms based on language pre-training.

3 Target Audience

Our tutorial is designed for the attendees of premier computational linguistics conferences, who preferably have interests and working experience in the processing of Asian languages and low-resource languages. The audiences would better have the following prerequisites.

- **Language Representation Learning**. Familiar with the basic concepts and main ideas of language pre-training, e.g., word embeddings (Mikolov et al., 2013), BERT (Devlin et al., 2019), and how the learned representations are employed to train various NLP tasks.
- **Linguistics**. Have the basic knowledge of the fundamental linguistic concepts (Jurafsky, 2000), e.g., *semantics*, *syntax*, *lexicography*, *morphology*, *phonetics*, etc.
- **Machine Learning.** Understand the traditional machine learning paradigm using handcrafted features (Svensén and Bishop, 2007) and the trendy deep learning-based methods (Goodfellow et al., 2016) allowing automatic feature learning in neural architectures.

4 Tutorial Outline (3 hours)

- PART I: Cantonese NLP overview (30 min).
  - Background of Cantonese.
  - Brief review of Cantonese NLP.
  - Brief introduction of language pre-training.
  - Problem definition and motivation.

• The outline of tutorial.

• PART II: Progress in language specificity, resources, and methodologies (40 min).
  • Brief history of Cantonese.
  • Linguistic characteristics of Cantonese.
  • Summary of Cantonese NLP resources.
  • Summary of Cantonese NLP methodologies.

• PART III: Pre-training in SOTA NLP (40 min).
  • Language pre-training methods.
  • Pre-training in low resource.
  • Chinese pre-training.

• PART IV: Challenges from colloquialism and multilingualism (40 min).
  • How colloquialism challenges pre-training.
  • How multilingualism challenges pre-training.

• PART V: Future NLP directions for Cantonese and other low-resource languages (30 min).
  • Summary of the tutorial.
  • Future work for Cantonese NLP and beyond.

5 Reading list

For trainees interested in reading important studies before the tutorial, we recommend the following: Ouyang (1993); Snow (2004); Sachs and Li (2007). Vaswani et al. (2017); Devlin et al. (2019); Liu et al. (2019); Brown et al. (2020); Sun et al. (2019); Liu et al. (2019); Nguyen et al. (2020).

6 Tutorial Presenters

Our tutorial will contain 5 parts and here we introduce the presenter for each of them.

• **Kam-Fai Wong** (*PART I*). Kam-Fai Wong a full professor in the Department of Systems Engineering and Engineering Management, The Chinese University of Hong Kong (CUHK). His research interest focuses on Chinese natural language processing and database. He is the fellow of ACL and has published over 260 technical papers in different international journals, conferences, and books. Also, He was the founding Editor-In-Chief of ACM Transactions on Asian Language Processing (TALIP) and the president of Asian Federation of Natural Language Processing (AFNLP).

• **Mingyu Wan** (*PART II*). Mingyu Wan is a postdoctoral fellow at the Department of Chinese and Bilingual Studies of Hong Kong Polytechnic University. Her research interest includes Financial NLP, CSR Modelling, Misinformation Detection, Sentiment/Emotion Analysis, Machine Learning, Language Resource Construction etc. She has 6 journal publications and more than 10 international conference proceedings in the NLP venue. She organizes the first Computing Social Responsibility Workshop cohosted at LREC 2022 conference.

• **Hanzhuo Tan** (*PART III*). Hanzhuo Tan is a Ph.D. student at the Department of Computing of Hong Kong Polytechnic University. His research interest includes self-supervised pre-training, NLP for social media, etc. He has 2 journal paper published in IEEE Transactions. He did six-month intership at Baidu PaddleNLP group on pre-training social transformer.

• **Rong Xiang** (*PART IV*). Rong Xiang is a postdoctoral fellow at the Department of Computing, Hong Kong Polytechnic University (PolyU). His research interests are acquisition and the application of human intelligence into machine learning networks. He has done substantial work in sentiment analysis, social media analysis and lexical semantics. He has published over 20 research papers in premier NLP venues. He co-organized CogALex 2020 and PACLIC 33.

• **Jing Li** (*PART V*). Jing Li is an assistant professor at the Department of Computing, Hong Kong Polytechnic University (PolyU). Before joining PolyU, she was a senior researcher in Tencent AI Lab. Her research interests are topic modeling, language representation learning, and NLP for colloquial and social media languages. She has published over 30 research papers in the top NLP venues and was invited to serve as the action editor for ACL rolling review (ARR) and the area chair for ACL 2021.

7 Other Information

Inclusion of Others' Work. This tutorial will survey the progress of Cantonese NLP and language pre-training, which substantially contain others' work.

Divergency considerations. Audiences who cannot speak Cantonese or Chinese will also be able to understand our tutorial. It will be conducted in English, where Cantonese cases will be presented with their English translations. Background knowledge will be provided to lower prerequisites (only those in Section 3 are needed). In the tutorial, we will discuss how the findings from Cantonese NLP can be generalized to other low-resource languages to benefit audiences in diverse streams.

Estimation of audience size. 100-200.

References

Tom B. Brown, Benjamin Mann, Nick Ryder, Melanie Subbiah, Jared Kaplan, Prafulla Dhariwal, Arvind Neelakantan, Pranav Shyam, Girish Sastry, Amanda Askell, Sandhini Agarwal, Ariel Herbert-Voss, Gretchen Krueger, Tom Henighan, Rewon Child, Aditya Ramesh, Daniel M. Ziegler, Jeffrey Wu, Clemens Winter, Christopher Hesse, Mark Chen, Eric Sigler, Mateusz Litwin, Scott Gray, Benjamin Chess, Jack Clark, Christopher Berner, Sam McCandlish, Alec Radford, Ilya Sutskever, and Dario Amodei. 2020. Language models are few-shot learners. In *Advances in Neural Information Processing Systems 33: Annual Conference on Neural Information Processing Systems 2020, NeurIPS 2020, December 6-12, 2020, virtual*.

Kevin Clark, Minh-Thang Luong, Quoc V. Le, and Christopher D. Manning. 2020. Electra: Pre-training text encoders as discriminators rather than generators. In *International Conference on Learning Representations*.

Yiming Cui, Wanxiang Che, Ting Liu, Bing Qin, and Ziqing Yang. 2021. Pre-training with whole word masking for chinese bert. *IEEE Transactions on Audio, Speech and Language Processing*.

Jacob Devlin, Ming-Wei Chang, Kenton Lee, and Kristina Toutanova. 2019. BERT: Pre-training of deep bidirectional transformers for language understanding. In *Proceedings of the 2019 Conference of the North American Chapter of the Association for Computational Linguistics: Human Language Technologies, Volume 1 (Long and Short Papers)*, pages 4171–4186, Minneapolis, Minnesota. Association for Computational Linguistics.

Annemarie Friedrich and Damyana Gateva. 2017. Classification of telicity using cross-linguistic annotation projection. In *Proceedings of the 2017 Conference on Empirical Methods in Natural Language Processing*, pages 2559–2565.

Ofelia García and Joshua A Fishman. 2011. *The multilingual apple: languages in New York City*. Walter de Gruyter.

Ian Goodfellow, Yoshua Bengio, and Aaron Courville. 2016. *Deep learning*. MIT press.

Michael A Hedderich, Lukas Lange, and Dietrich Klakow. 2021. Anea: distant supervision for low-resource named entity recognition. *arXiv preprint arXiv:2102.13129*.

Dan Jurafsky. 2000. *Speech & language processing*. Pearson Education India.

Shin Kataoka and Cream Lee. 2008. A system without a system: Cantonese romanization used in hong kong place and personal names. *Hong Kong Journal of Applied Linguistics*, 11(1):79–98.

Talaat Khalil, Kornel Kiełczewski, Georgios Christos Chouliaras, Amina Keldibek, and Maarten Versteegh. 2019. Cross-lingual intent classification in a low resource industrial setting. In *Proceedings of the 2019 Conference on Empirical Methods in Natural Language Processing and the 9th International Joint Conference on Natural Language Processing (EMNLP-IJCNLP)*, pages 6419–6424.

John Lee, Baikun Liang, and Haley Fong. 2021. Restatement and question generation for counsellor chatbot. In *Proceedings of the 1st Workshop on NLP for Positive Impact*, pages 1–7, Online. Association for Computational Linguistics.

Jing Li, Yan Song, Zhongyu Wei, and Kam-Fai Wong. 2018. A joint model of conversational discourse latent topics on microblogs. *Computational Linguistics*, 44(4):719–754.

Pierre Lison, Jeremy Barnes, Aliaksandr Hubin, and Samia Touileb. 2020. Named entity recognition without labelled data: A weak supervision approach. In *Proceedings of the 58th Annual Meeting of the Association for Computational Linguistics*, pages 1518–1533, Online. Association for Computational Linguistics.

Yinhan Liu, Myle Ott, Naman Goyal, Jingfei Du, Mandar Joshi, Danqi Chen, Omer Levy, Mike Lewis, Luke Zettlemoyer, and Veselin Stoyanov. 2019. Roberta: A robustly optimized BERT pretraining approach. *CoRR*, abs/1907.11692.

S. Matthews and V. Yip. 2011. Cantonese: A comprehensive grammar (2nd ed.). *Routledge Grammars*.

Tomas Mikolov, Wen-tau Yih, and Geoffrey Zweig. 2013. Linguistic regularities in continuous space word representations. In *Proceedings of the 2013 Conference of the North American Chapter of the Association for Computational Linguistics: Human Language Technologies*, pages 746–751, Atlanta, Georgia. Association for Computational Linguistics.

Dat Quoc Nguyen, Thanh Vu, and Anh-Tuan Nguyen. 2020. Bertweet: A pre-trained language model for english tweets. In *Proceedings of the 2020 Conference on Empirical Methods in Natural Language Processing: System Demonstrations*, pages 9–14.

Jueya Ouyang. 1993. Putonghua guangzhouhua de bijiao yu xuexi (the comparison and learning of mandarin and cantonese).

Alexander Ratner, Stephen H Bach, Henry Ehrenberg, Jason Fries, Sen Wu, and Christopher Ré. 2017. Snorkel: Rapid training data creation with weak supervision. In *Proceedings of the VLDB Endowment. International Conference on Very Large Data Bases*, 3, page 269. NIH Public Access.

Sebastian Riedel, Limin Yao, and Andrew McCallum. 2010. Modeling relations and their mentions without labeled text. In *Joint European Conference on Machine Learning and Knowledge Discovery in Databases*, pages 148–163. Springer.

Gertrude Tinker Sachs and David CS Li. 2007. Cantonese as an additional language in hong kong. *Multilingua*, 26(95):130.

Gözde Gül Şahin and Mark Steedman. 2018. Data augmentation via dependency tree morphing for low-resource languages. In *Proceedings of the 2018 Conference on Empirical Methods in Natural Language Processing*, pages 5004–5009.

Don Snow. 2004. *Cantonese as written language: The growth of a written Chinese vernacular*, volume 1. Hong Kong University Press.

Yu Sun, Shuohuan Wang, Yukun Li, Shikun Feng, Xuyi Chen, Han Zhang, Xin Tian, Danxiang Zhu, Hao Tian, and Hua Wu. 2019. Ernie: Enhanced representation through knowledge integration. *arXiv preprint arXiv:1904.09223*.

Markus Svensén and Christopher M Bishop. 2007. Pattern recognition and machine learning.

Ashish Vaswani, Noam Shazeer, Niki Parmar, Jakob Uszkoreit, Llion Jones, Aidan N Gomez, Łukasz Kaiser, and Illia Polosukhin. 2017. Attention is all you need. *Advances in neural information processing systems*, 30.

Guillaume Wisniewski, Nicolas Pécheux, Souhir Gahbiche-Braham, and François Yvon. 2014. Cross-lingual part-of-speech tagging through ambiguous learning. In *Proceedings of the 2014 Conference on Empirical Methods in Natural Language Processing (EMNLP)*, pages 1779–1785, Doha, Qatar. Association for Computational Linguistics.

Tak-sum Wong and John SY Lee. 2018. Register-sensitive translation: A case study of mandarin and cantonese (non-archival extended abstract). In *Proceedings of the 13th Conference of the Association for Machine Translation in the Americas (Volume 1: Research Track)*, pages 89–96.

Shijie Wu and Mark Dredze. 2020. Are all languages created equal in multilingual BERT? In *Proceedings of the 5th Workshop on Representation Learning for NLP*, pages 120–130, Online. Association for Computational Linguistics.

Rong Xiang, Ying Jiao, and Qin Lu. 2019. Sentiment augmented attention network for cantonese restaurant review analysis. In *Proceedings of the 8th KDD Workshop on Issues of Sentiment Discovery and Opinion Mining (WISDOM)*, pages 1–9. KDD WISDOM.

Henry Yu. 2013. Mountains of gold: Canada, north america, and the cantonese pacific. In *Routledge Handbook of the Chinese Diaspora*, pages 124–137. Routledge.

Meishan Zhang, Yue Zhang, and Guohong Fu. 2019. Cross-lingual dependency parsing using code-mixed TreeBank. In *Proceedings of the 2019 Conference on Empirical Methods in Natural Language Processing and the 9th International Joint Conference on Natural Language Processing (EMNLP-IJCNLP)*, pages 997–1006, Hong Kong, China. Association for Computational Linguistics.

Grounding Meaning Representation for Situated Reasoning

Nikhil Krishnaswamy
Department of Computer Science
Colorado State University
Fort Collins, CO USA
nkrishna@colostate.edu

James Pustejovsky
Department of Computer Science
Brandeis University
Waltham, MA USA
jamesp@brandeis.edu

1 Tutorial Description

As natural language technology becomes ever-present in everyday life, people will expect artificial agents to understand language use as humans do. Nevertheless, most advanced neural AI systems fail at some types of interactions that are trivial for humans (e.g., ask a smart system "What am I pointing at?"). One critical aspect of human language understanding is *situated reasoning*, where inferences make reference to the local context, perceptual surroundings, and contextual groundings from the interaction. In this **cutting-edge** tutorial, we bring to the NLP/CL community a synthesis of multimodal grounding and meaning representation techniques with formal and computational models of *embodied reasoning*. We will discuss existing approaches to multimodal language grounding and meaning representations, discuss the kind of information each method captures and their relative suitability to situated reasoning tasks, and demonstrate how to construct agents that conduct situated reasoning by embodying a simulated environment. In doing so, these agents also represent their human interlocutor(s) within the simulation, and are represented through their virtual embodiment in the real world, enabling true bidirectional communication with a computer using multiple modalities.

"Grounding" in much of the NLP literature involves linking linguistic expressions to information expressed in another modality, often images or video (Yatskar et al., 2016; Li et al., 2019). Examples include linking semantic roles to entities in an image, or joint linguistic-visual attention between a caption and an image or video. Efforts have also focused on creating common meaning representation formalisms for linguistic data that are known to be relatively expressive, easy to annotate, and extensible to accommodate linguistic diversity, scale, and support inference, e.g., Copestake et al. (2005); Banarescu et al. (2013); Cooper and Ginzburg (2015); Pustejovsky et al. (2019); Lai et al. (2021).

Robust human-computer interactions and human-robot interactions will require representations with all these features, that encode the different modalities in use in such an interaction and ground them to the shared environment, enabling bidirectional, symmetric communication, and shared reference. Central to such situated meaning is the recognition and interpretation of gesture in the common ground (Holler and Wilkin, 2009; Alahverdzhieva et al., 2018).

Certain problems in human-to-human communication cannot be solved without *situated reasoning*, meaning they cannot be adequately addressed with ungrounded meaning representation or cross-modal linking of instances alone. Examples include grounding an object and then reasoning with it ("Pick up *this* box. Put it *there*."), referring to a previously-established concept or instance that was never explicitly introduced into the dialogue, underspecification of deixis, and in general, dynamic updating of context through perceptual, linguistic, action, or self-announcement. Without *both* a representation framework and mechanism for grounding references and inferences to the environment, such problems may well remain out of reach for NLP.

An appropriate representation should accommodate both the structure and content of different modalities, as well as facilitate alignment and binding across them. However, it must also distinguish between alignment across channels in a multimodal dialogue (language, gesture, gaze), and the situated grounding of an expression to the local environment, be it objects in a situated context, an image, or a formal registration in a database. Therefore, such a meaning representation should also have the basic facility for situated grounding; i.e., explicit mention of object and situational state in context.

To date there has been interest in creating meaning representations that capture multimodality, and in multimodal corpora that capture language use in a situated environment (e.g., Chen et al.

Proceedings of the 2nd Conference of the Asia-Pacific Chapter of the Association for Computational Linguistics and the 12th International Joint Conference on Natural Language Processing: Tutorial Abstracts, pages 22–27
November 20-21, 2022.

(2019)), yet the two have been largely distinct. We will demonstrate how to bring these together into grounded meaning representations that capture language, gesture, object, and event semantics that can be used to not only represent situated meaning, but drive situated *reasoning* in embodied agents that occupy a three-dimensional environment.

There have been recent *ACL tutorials on meaning representations (Lopez and Gilroy, 2018; Koller et al., 2019), on common-sense reasoning (Sap et al., 2020), and on common ground and multimodality (Alikhani and Stone, 2020). To our knowledge this is the first time these three areas have been brought together with situated, grounded reasoning for an NLP/CL audience.

This tutorial will cover the most pressing problems in situated reasoning: namely, those requiring both multimodal grounding of expressions, as well as contextual reasoning with this information. Three example areas we will cover are:

"Make Me Another" Grounding an underspecified item or concept to previous elements of a dialogue requires an understanding of both what is salient in context, and of what elements of that item or concept are relevant to the situation inhabited by the interlocutors (Schlangen and Skantze, 2011). For example, if someone is cooking a stack of pancakes for someone else, and the diner says "make me *another*," a human would likely infer a reference to a single pancake, not the whole stack. The computational mechanisms for representing the elements of the environment and making this inference are richly involved. Addressing this problem and similar ones is an important part of building agents that respond to queries and requests in ways that are situationally appropriate.

Underspecification of Deixis The referent of a deixis may be ambiguous, though it naturally grounds to an object if one is available (Alahverdzhieva and Lascarides, 2011). Adding demonstratives like "this" or "there" naturally selects for objects vs. locations, and we will present models to capture these joint gesture-language semantics (Alahverdzhieva and Lascarides, 2010). Even coupling gesture and language may be insufficient for reasoning. "Pick up *this one* and put *it* · *there*," plus deixis, singles out a liftable object in the embedding space, and a possible ambiguity. If *there* refers to a location, then the command can be fully grounded in space. But, if the referent of the deixis is an object, additional reasoning must be conducted vis-à-vis what part of the object accommodates both the action *put* and the denotatum of *this one*. The many possible interpretations lead to rich reasoning strategies in situated space.

Dynamic Updating of Context Through Announcement When a participant in a dialogue sees, says, does, or realizes something new, the external and/or internal world changes for the participants, along with the capabilities for reasoning over the situation. For example, someone can verbally or gesturally announce an intent or provide information; perceptually demonstrate that something is present or absent; visibly act on a request or command; and personally realize something based on the current context. Each of these requires situated grounding and reasoning within those worlds.

1.1 Outline

This tutorial comprises 4 45-minute parts. 1) We will first present existing approaches to multimodal grounding, in the form of cross-modal linking (Yatskar et al., 2016; Yang et al., 2016; Sadhu et al., 2021) or linguistic-visual attention (Antol et al., 2015; Shih et al., 2016; Zhu et al., 2018; Sood et al., 2020) along with datasets that exist for this purpose (e.g., Kontogiorgos et al., 2018; Chen et al., 2019; Shridhar et al., 2020), and 2) common approaches to structured meaning representation (Copestake et al., 2005; Banarescu et al., 2013; Cooper and Ginzburg, 2015). 3) We will describe the forumation of *common ground* as a data structure of the information associated with a state in a dialogue or discourse (Clark et al., 1983; Stalnaker, 2002), and how it can be used to ground elements like gestures and situations to meaning representations (Lascarides and Stone, 2009; Alahverdzhieva et al., 2018). Each section will focus the material with regard how the discussed frameworks treat the grounding and reasoning questions from Sec. 1.

4) Finally we will present some of own work, including the grounded modeling language VoxML (Pustejovsky and Krishnaswamy, 2016) and a demonstration of building agents capable of situated reasoning in *VoxWorld* (Krishnaswamy and Pustejovsky, 2016; Pustejovsky and Krishnaswamy, 2021), a platform built on VoxML for developing embodied agent behaviors. We will provide a starter scene with an agent who can act upon the world, and discuss the computational and modeling considerations that go into developing

distinct types of agents, such as virtual collaborative assistants (Krishnaswamy et al., 2017), mobile robots (Krajovic et al., 2020; Tellex et al., 2020), and self-guided exploratory agents (Tan et al., 2019; Pustejovsky and Krishnaswamy, 2022), comparing our own framework to others'.

Technical requirements We have no special hardware requirements for this tutorial except for a projector or display screen.

Distribution of materials We plan to make all tutorial materials fully available to the community.

2 Target and Expected Audience

This tutorial will be of interest to both researchers in meaning representation, and in multimodal NLP and grounding, particularly those interested in both theoretical and data-driven approaches to language grounding and those interested in treating automated reasoning as more than just a pure machine learning problem. The diverse approaches to linguistic grounding of situated meaning have also provoked significant interest from the robotics community. Given the increased interest in interactive agents and grounding for robotics at in the *ACL community, as witnessed by the recent creation of Language Grounding to Vision, Robotics, and Beyond tracks at most *ACL venues, this tutorial, that synthesizes various approaches to situated conversation and interaction will be a timely way to bring these two communities closer. We expect this tutorial will draw an audience of roughly 30-45.

2.1 Requisite Background

This tutorial will be self-contained. However, to get the most out of this tutorial, attendees will want to be familiar with both theoretical and machine-learning approaches to semantics. Familiarity with common meaning representation frameworks, such as abstract meaning representation (Banarescu et al., 2013) or minimal recursion semantics (Copestake et al., 2005), is desirable, as is familiarity with multimodal language and vision techniques, such as VQA or image captioning (Antol et al., 2015; Shih et al., 2016). Participants will be invited to "code along" for the last part of the tutorial if they so desire, for which knowledge of C# and the Unity game engine will be advantageous but *not* prerequisite.

3 Breadth and Reading List

This tutorial draws on a wealth of both theory and applied research in multimodal semantics, including not only the central meaning representation work mentioned above (Copestake et al., 2005; Banarescu et al., 2013; Cooper and Ginzburg, 2015; Pustejovsky et al., 2019), but also gesture semantics and situated dialogue (Kendon, 2004; Lascarides and Stone, 2006, 2009; Kelleher and Kruijff, 2006), and qualitative spatiotemporal reasoning (Freksa, 1991; Forbus et al., 1991; Zimmermann and Freksa, 1996; Cohn and Renz, 2008). We bring these diverse areas together in the modeling language VoxML (Pustejovsky and Krishnaswamy, 2016), and this tutorial will demonstrate how to exploit the strengths of both meaning representations and data-driven multimodal methods to create agents that reason with vision, language, action, and gesture about the environments they inhabit and share with human beings. Suggested reading is below:

- L. Banarescu, et al. (2013). Abstract meaning representation for sembanking. In Proceedings of the 7th Linguistic Annotation Workshop and Interoperability with Discourse, pages 178–186. `https://aclanthology.org/W13-2322.pdf`
- A. Copestake, et al. (2005). Minimal recursion semantics: An introduction. Research on Language and Computation, 3(2):281–332. `https://doi.org/10.1007/s11168-006-6327-9`
- R. Cooper and J. Ginzburg. (2015). Type theory with records for natural language semantics. The Handbook of Contemporary Semantic Theory, pages 375–407. `https://doi.org/10.1002/9781118882139.ch12`
- A. Lascarides and M. Stone. (2009). A formal semantic analysis of gesture. Journal of Semantics, 26(4), 393-449. `https://homepages.inf.ed.ac.uk/alex/papers/gesture_formal.pdf`
- K. Alahverdzhieva, et al. Aligning speech and co-speech gesture in a constraint-based grammar. `https://jlm.ipipan.waw.pl/index.php/JLM/article/view/167/179`
- The qualitative spatial dynamics of motion in language. J. Pustejovsky, and J. L. Moszkowicz. (2011). Spatial Cognition & Computation 11, no. 1 (2011): 15-44. `http://www.cs-135.org/wp-content/uploads/2017/12/SCC-2011.pdf`

- J. Pustejovsky and N. Krishnaswamy (2021). Situated Meaning in Multimodal Dialogue: Human-Robot and Human-Computer Interactions, in TAL Volume 61 issue 3, pp 17-41. https://www.atala.org/sites/default/files/TAL-61-3-1_Pustejovsky.pdf
- J. Pustejovsky and N. Krishnaswamy (2021). Embodied Human Computer Interaction, Künstliche Intelligenz, Springer. https://doi.org/10.1007/s13218-021-00727-5

4 Instructors

Nikhil Krishnaswamy is Assistant Professor of Computer Science at Colorado State University and director of the Situated Grounding and Natural Language Lab (www.signallab.ai). He received his Ph.D. from Brandeis University in 2017. His primary research is in situated grounding and natural language semantics, using computational, formal, and simulation methods to study how language works and how humans use it. He is the co-creator of VoxML. He has taught courses on machine learning and NLP, previously taught at EACL 2017 (with J. Pustejovsky), and he will be co-teaching (also with J. Pustejovsky) at ESSLLI 2022 on multimodal semantics of affordances and actions. He has routinely received positive feedback as an instructor, including "always willing to engage in in-depth discussions regarding class material," "his understanding of the subject matter is phenomenal," "my favorite course this semester," and "he clearly spends a lot of time making his lectures engaging." He has served on the PC for ACL, EACL, NAACL, EMNLP, AAAI, AACL, etc. Email: nkrishna@colostate.edu, Website: https://www.nikhilkrishnaswamy.com.

James Pustejovsky is the TJX Feldberg Chair in Computer Science at Brandeis University, where he is also Chair of the Linguistics Program, Chair of the Computational Linguistics M.S. Program, and Director of the Lab for Linguistics and Computation. He received his B.S. from MIT and his Ph.D. from UMass Amherst. He has worked on computational and lexical semantics for 25 years and is chief developer of Generative Lexicon Theory; the TARSQI platform for temporal reasoning in language; TimeML and ISO-TimeML, a recently adopted ISO standard for temporal information in language; the recently adopted standard ISO-Space, a specification for spatial information in language; and the co-creator of the VoxML modeling framework for linguistic expressions and interactions as multimodal simulations VoxML (co-created with N. Krishnaswamy), enables real-time communication between humans and computers or robots for joint tasks, utilizing speech, gesture, gaze, and action. He is currently working with robotics researchers in HRI to allow the VoxML platform to act as both a dialogue management system as well as a simulation environment that reveals realtime epistemic state and perceptual input to a computational agent. Email: jamesp@brandeis.edu, Website: https://www.pusto.com.

5 Diversity

Situated reasoning and grounding inherently crosses language boundaries. Language grounding in English can be compared to language grounding a low-resourced language by way of a situated model. From a research perspective these are important questions to answer, to explore how different languages represent the same environment or situation. Therefore situated reasoning is an important potential way to broaden the linguistic diversity of NLP, and we hope the meaning representation component of this tutorial may inspire broadening meaning representations to more languages yet.

The instructors are junior and senior faculty, respectively, established in the NLP community. We actively recruit women and underrepresented minorities to our respective research groups, and plan to promote this tutorial to an international and diverse audience. We are experienced instructors in a hybrid format, and we will accommodate and promote remote attendance to broaden participation.

6 Ethics Statement

Computational agents that reason situationally necessarily require sight and hearing, and come with concomitant ethical issues regarding computer vision and speech recognition. In the course of this tutorial, we will discuss many of the considerations surrounding user privacy and storing user data (or, in the case of our own research, explicitly *not* doing that (Wang et al., 2017)). We will also discuss adapting speech recognition models to user diversity as part of the multimodal grounding section (Krishnaswamy and Alalyani, 2021).

Real-time, situated reasoning requires smaller, lightweight models. While we use large models where necessary, our use of meaning representations to guide search within multimodal grounding tasks provides a way to accomplish this task with less computational overhead and resource use.

References

Katya Alahverdzhieva and Alex Lascarides. 2010. Analysing speech and co-speech gesture in constraint-based grammars. In *The Proceedings of the 17th International Conference on Head-Driven Phrase Structure Grammar*, pages 6–26. Citeseer.

Katya Alahverdzhieva and Alex Lascarides. 2011. An hpsg approach to synchronous speech and deixis. In *Proceedings of the 18th international conference on head-driven phase structure grammar (HPSG)*, pages 6–24. CSLI Publications.

Katya Alahverdzhieva, Alex Lascarides, and Dan Flickinger. 2018. Aligning speech and co-speech gesture in a constraint-based grammar. *Journal of Language Modelling*, 5(3):421–464.

Malihe Alikhani and Matthew Stone. 2020. Achieving common ground in multi-modal dialogue. In *Proceedings of the 58th Annual Meeting of the Association for Computational Linguistics: Tutorial Abstracts*, pages 10–15.

Stanislaw Antol, Aishwarya Agrawal, Jiasen Lu, Margaret Mitchell, Dhruv Batra, C Lawrence Zitnick, and Devi Parikh. 2015. Vqa: Visual question answering. In *Proceedings of the IEEE international conference on computer vision*, pages 2425–2433.

Laura Banarescu, Claire Bonial, Shu Cai, Madalina Georgescu, Kira Griffitt, Ulf Hermjakob, Kevin Knight, Philipp Koehn, Martha Palmer, and Nathan Schneider. 2013. Abstract meaning representation for sembanking. In *Proceedings of the 7th linguistic annotation workshop and interoperability with discourse*, pages 178–186.

Howard Chen, Alane Suhr, Dipendra Misra, Noah Snavely, and Yoav Artzi. 2019. Touchdown: Natural language navigation and spatial reasoning in visual street environments. In *Proceedings of the IEEE/CVF Conference on Computer Vision and Pattern Recognition*, pages 12538–12547.

Herbert H Clark, Robert Schreuder, and Samuel Buttrick. 1983. Common ground at the understanding of demonstrative reference. *Journal of verbal learning and verbal behavior*, 22(2):245–258.

Anthony G Cohn and Jochen Renz. 2008. Qualitative spatial representation and reasoning. *Foundations of Artificial Intelligence*, 3:551–596.

Robin Cooper and Jonathan Ginzburg. 2015. Type theory with records for natural language semantics. *The handbook of contemporary semantic theory*, pages 375–407.

Ann Copestake, Dan Flickinger, Carl Pollard, and Ivan A Sag. 2005. Minimal recursion semantics: An introduction. *Research on language and computation*, 3(2):281–332.

Kenneth D Forbus, Paul Nielsen, and Boi Faltings. 1991. Qualitative spatial reasoning: The clock project. *Artificial Intelligence*, 51(1-3):417–471.

Christian Freksa. 1991. Qualitative spatial reasoning. In *Cognitive and linguistic aspects of geographic space*, pages 361–372. Springer.

Judith Holler and Katie Wilkin. 2009. Communicating common ground: How mutually shared knowledge influences speech and gesture in a narrative task. *Language and Cognitive Processes*, 24(2):267–289.

John Kelleher and Geert-Jan M Kruijff. 2006. Incremental generation of spatial referring expressions in situated dialog. In *Proceedings of the 21st international conference on computational linguistics and 44th annual meeting of the association for computational linguistics*, pages 1041–1048.

Adam Kendon. 2004. *Gesture: Visible action as utterance*. Cambridge University Press.

Alexander Koller, Stephan Oepen, and Weiwei Sun. 2019. Graph-based meaning representations: Design and processing. In *Proceedings of the 57th Annual Meeting of the Association for Computational Linguistics: Tutorial Abstracts*, pages 6–11.

Dimosthenis Kontogiorgos, Vanya Avramova, Simon Alexanderson, Patrik Jonell, Catharine Oertel, Jonas Beskow, Gabriel Skantze, and Joakim Gustafson. 2018. A multimodal corpus for mutual gaze and joint attention in multiparty situated interaction. In *Proceedings of the Eleventh International Conference on Language Resources and Evaluation (LREC 2018)*.

Katherine Krajovic, Nikhil Krishnaswamy, Nathaniel J Dimick, R Pito Salas, and James Pustejovsky. 2020. Situated multimodal control of a mobile robot: Navigation through a virtual environment. *arXiv preprint arXiv:2007.09053*.

Nikhil Krishnaswamy and Nada Alalyani. 2021. Embodied multimodal agents to bridge the understanding gap. In *Proceedings of the First Workshop on Bridging Human–Computer Interaction and Natural Language Processing*, pages 41–46.

Nikhil Krishnaswamy, Pradyumna Narayana, Isaac Wang, Kyeongmin Rim, Rahul Bangar, Dhruva Patil, Gururaj Mulay, Ross Beveridge, Jaime Ruiz, Bruce Draper, et al. 2017. Communicating and acting: Understanding gesture in simulation semantics. In *IWCS 2017—12th International Conference on Computational Semantics—Short papers*.

Nikhil Krishnaswamy and James Pustejovsky. 2016. Voxsim: A visual platform for modeling motion language. In *Proceedings of COLING 2016, the 26th International Conference on Computational Linguistics: System Demonstrations*, pages 54–58.

Kenneth Lai, Richard Brutti, Lucia Donatelli, and James Pustejovsky. 2021. Situated umr for multimodal interactions. In *Proceedings of the 25th Workshop on the Semantics and Pragmatics of Dialogue*.

Alex Lascarides and Matthew Stone. 2006. *Formal semantics for iconic gesture*. Universität Potsdam.

Alex Lascarides and Matthew Stone. 2009. A formal semantic analysis of gesture. *Journal of Semantics*, 26(4):393–449.

Liunian Harold Li, Mark Yatskar, Da Yin, Cho-Jui Hsieh, and Kai-Wei Chang. 2019. Visualbert: A simple and performant baseline for vision and language. *arXiv preprint arXiv:1908.03557*.

Adam Lopez and Sorcha Gilroy. 2018. Graph formalisms for meaning representations. In *Proceedings of the 2018 Conference on Empirical Methods in Natural Language Processing: Tutorial Abstracts*.

James Pustejovsky and Nikhil Krishnaswamy. 2016. Voxml: A visualization modeling language. In *Proceedings of the Tenth International Conference on Language Resources and Evaluation (LREC'16)*, pages 4606–4613.

James Pustejovsky and Nikhil Krishnaswamy. 2021. Embodied human computer interaction. *KI-Künstliche Intelligenz*, pages 1–21.

James Pustejovsky and Nikhil Krishnaswamy. 2022. Multimodal semantics for affordances and actiona. In *International Conference on Human-Computer Interaction*. Springer.

James Pustejovsky, Ken Lai, and Nianwen Xue. 2019. Modeling quantification and scope in abstract meaning representations. In *Proceedings of the first international workshop on designing meaning representations*, pages 28–33.

Arka Sadhu, Tanmay Gupta, Mark Yatskar, Ram Nevatia, and Aniruddha Kembhavi. 2021. Visual semantic role labeling for video understanding. In *Proceedings of the IEEE/CVF Conference on Computer Vision and Pattern Recognition*, pages 5589–5600.

Maarten Sap, Vered Shwartz, Antoine Bosselut, Yejin Choi, and Dan Roth. 2020. Introductory tutorial: Commonsense reasoning for natural language processing. *Association for Computational Linguistics (ACL 2020): Tutorial Abstracts*, 27.

David Schlangen and Gabriel Skantze. 2011. A general, abstract model of incremental dialogue processing. *Dialogue & Discourse*, 2(1):83–111.

Kevin J Shih, Saurabh Singh, and Derek Hoiem. 2016. Where to look: Focus regions for visual question answering. In *Proceedings of the IEEE conference on computer vision and pattern recognition*, pages 4613–4621.

Mohit Shridhar, Jesse Thomason, Daniel Gordon, Yonatan Bisk, Winson Han, Roozbeh Mottaghi, Luke Zettlemoyer, and Dieter Fox. 2020. Alfred: A benchmark for interpreting grounded instructions for everyday tasks. In *Proceedings of the IEEE/CVF conference on computer vision and pattern recognition*, pages 10740–10749.

Ekta Sood, Simon Tannert, Philipp Müller, and Andreas Bulling. 2020. Improving natural language processing tasks with human gaze-guided neural attention. *Advances in Neural Information Processing Systems*, 33:6327–6341.

Robert Stalnaker. 2002. Common ground. *Linguistics and philosophy*, 25(5/6):701–721.

Hao Tan, Licheng Yu, and Mohit Bansal. 2019. Learning to navigate unseen environments: Back translation with environmental dropout. In *Proceedings of the 2019 Conference of the North American Chapter of the Association for Computational Linguistics: Human Language Technologies, Volume 1 (Long and Short Papers)*, pages 2610–2621.

Stefanie Tellex, Nakul Gopalan, Hadas Kress-Gazit, and Cynthia Matuszek. 2020. Robots that use language. *Annual Review of Control, Robotics, and Autonomous Systems*, 3:25–55.

Isaac Wang, Mohtadi Ben Fraj, Pradyumna Narayana, Dhruva Patil, Gururaj Mulay, Rahul Bangar, J Ross Beveridge, Bruce A Draper, and Jaime Ruiz. 2017. Eggnog: A continuous, multi-modal data set of naturally occurring gestures with ground truth labels. In *2017 12th IEEE International Conference on Automatic Face & Gesture Recognition (FG 2017)*, pages 414–421. IEEE.

Shaohua Yang, Qiaozi Gao, Changsong Liu, Caiming Xiong, Song-Chun Zhu, and Joyce Chai. 2016. Grounded semantic role labeling. In *Proceedings of the 2016 Conference of the North American Chapter of the Association for Computational Linguistics: Human Language Technologies*, pages 149–159.

Mark Yatskar, Luke Zettlemoyer, and Ali Farhadi. 2016. Situation recognition: Visual semantic role labeling for image understanding. *In Proceedings of the Conference of Computer Vision and Pattern Recognition (CVPR)*.

Junnan Zhu, Haoran Li, Tianshang Liu, Yu Zhou, Jiajun Zhang, and Chengqing Zong. 2018. Msmo: Multimodal summarization with multimodal output. In *Proceedings of the 2018 conference on empirical methods in natural language processing*, pages 4154–4164.

Kai Zimmermann and Christian Freksa. 1996. Qualitative spatial reasoning using orientation, distance, and path knowledge. *Applied intelligence*, 6(1):49–58.

The Battlefront of Combating Misinformation and Coping with Media Bias

Yi R. Fung[1], Kung-Hsiang Huang[1], Preslav Nakov[2], Heng Ji[1]
[1]University of Illinois Urbana-Champaign
[2]Mohamed bin Zayed University of Artificial Intelligence
{yifung2, khhuang3, hengji}@illinois.edu
preslav.nakov@mbzuai.ac.ae

Abstract

Misinformation is a pressing issue in modern society. It arouses a mixture of anger, distrust, confusion, and anxiety that cause damage on our daily life judgments and public policy decisions. While recent studies have explored various fake news detection and media bias detection techniques in attempts to tackle the problem, there remain many ongoing challenges yet to be addressed, as can be witnessed from the plethora of untrue and harmful content present during the COVID-19 pandemic and the international crises of late. In this tutorial, we provide researchers and practitioners with a systematic overview of the frontier in fighting misinformation. Specifically, we dive into the important research questions of how to (*i*) develop a robust fake news detection system, which not only fact-check information pieces provable by background knowledge but also reason about the consistency and the reliability of subtle details for emerging events; (*ii*) uncover the bias and agenda of news sources to better characterize misinformation; as well as (*iii*) correct false information and mitigate news bias, while allowing diverse opinions to be expressed. Moreover, we discuss the remaining challenges, future research directions, and exciting opportunities to help make this world a better place, with safer and more harmonic information sharing.

1 Introduction

The growth of online platforms has greatly facilitated the way people communicate with each other and stay informed about trending events. However, it has also spawned unprecedented levels of inaccurate or misleading information, as traditional journalism gate-keeping fails to keep up with the pace of media dissemination. These undesirable phenomena have caused societies to be torn over irrational beliefs, money lost from impulsive stock market moves, and deaths occurred that could have been avoided during the COVID-19 pandemic, due to the infodemic that came forth with it, etc. (Allcott and Gentzkow, 2017; Rapoza; Solomon et al., 2020). Even people who do not believe the misinformation may still be plagued by the pollution of unhealthy content surrounding them, an unpleasant situation known as *information disorder* (Wardle et al., 2018). Thus, it is of pertinent interest for our community to better understand, and to develop effective mechanisms for remedying misinformation and biased reporting.

The emerging nature of news events, which also span diverse domains (e.g., economy, military, health, sports, etc.) and reporting style (e.g., long text vs. short text, realistic image vs. artistic image, etc.), makes misinformation detection and characterization challenging. Combating fake news and biased reports involve an interdisciplinary research area of reasoning on the semantics, style, cross-media contextualization, background knowledge, and propagation patterns, among others (Saquete et al., 2020; Pennycook and Rand, 2021; Collins et al., 2021). Moreover, the recent trends towards a more comprehensive understanding of the source stance, reporting intent, target audience, and propaganda technique behind a problematic piece of news (Zhang and Ghorbani, 2020) require greater socio-cultural norm and common sense awareness.

In this half-day tutorial, we aim to present a systematic overview of technological advancement in tackling interconnected tasks related to misinformation, media bias, malicious intent monitoring, and corrective actions. First, we will review prevailing paradigms and data resources for misinformation detection and characterization. Moreover, we will discuss the latest approaches to automatically explain why a news piece is inaccurate or misleading, and perform rectification of biased reporting. The participants will learn about trends and emerging challenges, representative deep neural network models, ready-to-use training resources, as well as how state-of-the-art language (and multimedia)

Proceedings of the 2nd Conference of the Asia-Pacific Chapter of the Association for Computational Linguistics and the 12th International Joint Conference on Natural Language Processing: Tutorial Abstracts, pages 28–34

techniques can help build applications for the social good.

2 Outline of Tutorial Content

2.1 Background and Motivation [20min]

We begin motivating the tutorial topic with a selection of real-world examples of fake news and their harmful impacts to society, followed by a pedagogical exercise of how humans tend to approach the problem of fake news detection, characterization, and correction. We will point out conceptual distinctions amongst various types of fake news, including serious fabrication in news journalism about misattributed or nonexisting events, oversensationalized clickbaits, hoaxes which are false with the intention to be picked up by traditional news websites and satire which mimic genuine news but contain irony and absurdity (Rubin et al., 2015). For example, in general, news articles more likely involve serious fabrications, while social media posts involve more humour such as satire and hoaxes. We will also describe the cognitive, social and affective factors that lead people to form or endorse misinformed views (e.g., intuitive thinking, illusory truths, source cues, emotions, etc.), and the psychological barriers to knowledge revision after misinformation has been corrected, including correction not integrated, selective retrieval, and continued influence theories (Ecker et al., 2022).

2.2 Fake News Detection [60min]

Bearing these properties in mind, we introduce:

- ***stylistic*** approaches that focus on lexical features, readability, and syntactic clues (Pérez-Rosas et al., 2018; Rashkin et al., 2017; Choshen et al., 2019)

- ***fact-checking*** approaches that compare check-worthy content with background knowledge, such as external knowledge bases (FreeBase, WikiBase, etc) and previously fact-checked claims (Baly et al., 2018; Shaar et al., 2020; Hu et al., 2021; Liu et al., 2021; Guo et al., 2022)

- ***semantic-consistency*** approaches that extract features related to single-document discourse-level coherence (Karimi and Tang, 2019) and cross-document event-centric coherence (Wu et al., 2022) in text. Extending to cross-media domain, the common strategy is to check text–image consistency (Tan et al., 2020; Huang et al., 2022; Aneja et al., 2021) and text–video consistency (Wang et al., 2022).

- ***propagation patterns*** that capture confounding factors from the dynamics of how a news topic spreads and the social network interactions (Lu and Li, 2020; Shu et al., 2020; Cheng et al., 2021).

We will discuss the merits and the limitations of these different lines of fake news detection approaches. For example, fact-checking approaches may not fare well for early rumours or breaking news not yet groundable to an established background knowledge (Zhou et al., 2019; Guo et al., 2022), in which case, the credibility of the news source can offer complementary assistance (Cheng et al., 2021). Stylistic approaches may be simple but yet effective for detecting low-quality human-written fake news, but not so good for machine-generated misinformation, which is stylistically consistent regardless of the underlying motives (Schuster et al., 2020). We then cover recent approaches (Lee et al., 2021b; Fung et al., 2021) that leverage a combination of these elements for greater representation power and robustness. Importantly, we also cover works that explore the diachronic bias of fake news detection and portability across data in different time and language settings (Murayama et al., 2021; Gereme et al., 2021).

Special Note on Neural Fake News Generation & Detection:
Advancements in natural language generation spawn the rise of news generation models which represent a double-edged sword (Zellers et al., 2019). On one hand, malicious actors may irresponsibility take advantage of the technology to influence opinions and gain revenue. But, on the other hand, it can also be used as a source of machine-synthesized training data for detector models to overcome data scarcity since real-world fake news tends to be eventually removed by platforms, as well as a tool for threat modeling to develop proactive defenses against potential threats. We review how popular detectors perform on fake news created from large-scale language and vision generator model (Zellers et al., 2019; Güera and Delp, 2018; Agarwal et al., 2019). We also review progress in

generating fake news that better aligns with the key topic and facts (Mosallanezhad et al., 2021; Shu et al., 2021; Fung et al., 2021), and work towards applying topic/fact-constrained fake news generation to construct silver-standard data annotations for finer-grained fake news detection (Fung et al., 2021).

2.3 Fake News Characterization [30min]

To better understand and fight fake news, we next address some fundamental questions of characterizing fake news based on underlying source bias, reporting agenda, propaganda techniques, and target audience (Buchanan, 2020). First, we introduce modeling approaches for detecting political and socio-cultural biases in news articles (Kulkarni et al., 2018; Fan et al., 2019; Baly et al., 2020; Forbes et al., 2020). Next, we introduce the recent EMU benchmark that require models to answer open-ended questions capturing the intent and the implications of a media edit (Da et al., 2021). We cover methodologies for identifying the specific propaganda techniques used, *e.g.*, *smears*, *glittering generalities*, *association transfer*, etc. (Dimitrov et al., 2021). We also discuss the latest explorations in predicting the intended target of harmful media content, *e.g.*, the person, the organization, the community, or the society level (Pramanick et al., 2021).

2.4 Corrective Actions for Misinformation and Biased News Reporting [30min]

After misinformation has been detected and categorized based on its various characteristics, there is naturally follow-up interest in corrective explanations on why a piece of information is fake or misleading, and how to report less biased and more comprehensive news in general. Hence, we cover frameworks for explaining why a given piece of news is actually fake news through the leverage of reader comments, as well as appropriate strategies for placing the corrective explanations based on user studies (Shu et al., 2019; Brashier et al., 2021). We also cover research on mitigating media bias, such as through neutral article generation (Lee et al., 2021a).

Industry Initiatives: We further point out recent actions by tech companies with media-hosting platforms for fighting fake news. With urges from the government, they experiment with removing economic incentives for traffickers of misinformation, promoting media literacy, suspending improper posts and accounts, and adding colored labels, with corrections constructed from a community-based point system similar to Wikipedia, directly beneath misinformation posted by public figures[1].

2.5 Concluding Remarks & Future Directions [30min]

Finally, we summarize the major remaining challenges in this space, including the detection of subtle inconsistencies, enforcing schema or logical constraints in the detection, identifying semantically consistent but misattributed cross-media pairings, and greater precision in fine-grained explanations for the detected misinformation.

3 Specification of the Tutorial

The proposed tutorial is a cutting-edge tutorial that introduces new frontiers in research on battling misinformation and news bias. The presented topic has not been covered by previous ACL/NAACL/AACL tutorials in the past four years. While there has been an EMNLP'20 tutorial on "Fact-Checking, Fake News, Propaganda, and Media Bias: Truth Seeking in the Post-Truth Era" (Nakov and Da San Martino, 2020) and a COLING'20 tutorial on "Detection and Resolution of Rumors and Misinformation with NLP" (Derczynski and Zubiaga, 2020), fake news is a continuously evolving and extremely important societal problem. In our tutorial, we place particular emphasis on the latest lines of development, including an emphasis on multimedia contextualization, sociocultural awareness in characterization, and corrective actions. We estimate at least 75% of the work we reference has not been covered in the two previous aforementioned tutorials. We further estimate that at least 75% of the research covered in this tutorial is by researchers other than the instructors.

Audience and Prerequisites Based on the level of interest in this topic, we expect around 100 participants. While no specific background knowledge is assumed of the audience, it would be best for the attendees to know basic deep learning, pre-trained word embeddings (e.g., Word2Vec) and language models (e.g., BERT).

Reading List We recommend the literature cited in this paper, particularly: the rising threats of neural fake news (Zellers et al., 2019; Chawla, 2019),

[1] https://www.nbcnews.com/tech/tech-news/twitter-testing-new-ways-fight-misinformation-including-community-based-points-n1139931

knowledge-driven misinformation detection (Hu et al., 2021; Fung et al., 2021; Guo et al., 2022), intent characterization (Buchanan, 2020; Da et al., 2021), and study of fake news impact from a psychological point of view (Ecker et al., 2022).

Desired Venue The most desired venue for this tutorial would be AACL-IJCNLP'2022. The majority of our tutorial speakers have educational experience in Asia. At the same time, we also represent a global diversity in our research work.

Open Access We agree to allow the publication of the tutorial materials and presentation in the ACL Anthology. All the materials will be openly available at the UIUC Blender Lab website.

4 Tutorial Instructors

Below, we give the biographies of the speakers.

Yi R. Fung is a second-year Ph.D. student at the Computer Science Department of UIUC, with research interests in knowledge reasoning, misinformation detection, and computation for the social good. Her recent works include the INFOSURGEON fake news detection framework, and multiview news summarization. Yi is a recipient of the NAACL'21 Best Demo Paper, the UIUC Lauslen and Andrew fellowship, and the National Association of Asian American Professionals Future Leaders award. She has also been previously selected for invited talk (1 hour presentation) at the Harvard Medical School Bioinformatics Seminar. Additional information is available at `https://yrf1.github.io`.

Kung-Hsiang Huang is a first-year Ph.D. student at the Computer Science Department of UIUC. His research focuses on fact-checking and fake news detection. Prior to joining UIUC, he obtained his B.Eng. in Computer Science from the Hong Kong University of Science and Technology, and his M.S. in Computer Science is from USC. He is also a co-founder of an AI startup, Rosetta.ai. Additional information is available at `https://khuangaf.github.io`.

Preslav Nakov is a Principal Scientist at the Qatar Computing Research Institute (QCRI), HBKU, who received his PhD degree from the University of California at Berkeley (supported by a Fulbright grant). Dr. Nakov is President of ACL SIGLEX, Secretary of ACL SIGSLAV, a member of the EACL advisory board, as well as a member of the editorial board of Computational Linguistics, TACL, CS&L, IEEE TAC, NLE, AI Communications, and Frontiers in AI. His research on fake news was featured by over 100 news outlets, including Forbes, Boston Globe, Aljazeera, MIT Technology Review, Science Daily, Popular Science, The Register, WIRED, and Engadget, among others. He has driven relevant tutorials such as:

- WSDM'22: Fact-Checking, Fake News, Propaganda, Media Bias, and the COVID-19 Infodemic.
- CIKM'21: Fake News, Disinformation, Propaganda, and Media Bias.
- EMNLP'20: Fact-Checking, Fake News, Propaganda, and Media Bias: Truth Seeking in the Post-Truth Era.

Additional information is available at `https://en.wikipedia.org/wiki/Preslav_Nakov`.

Heng Ji is a Professor at the Computer Science Department of the University of Illinois Urbana-Champaign, and an Amazon Scholar. Her research interests focus on NLP, especially on Multimedia Multilingual Information Extraction, Knowledge Base Population and Knowledge-driven Generation. She was selected as "Young Scientist" and a member of the Global Future Council on the Future of Computing by the World Economic Forum. The awards she received include "AI's 10 to Watch" Award, NSF CAREER award, Google Research Award, IBM Watson Faculty Award, Bosch Research Award, Amazon AWS Award, ACL2020 Best Demo Paper Award, and NAACL2021 Best Demo Paper Award. She has given a large number of keynotes and 20 tutorials on Information Extraction, Natural Language Understanding, and Knowledge Base Construction in many conferences including but not limited to ACL, EMNLP, NAACL, NeurIPS, AAAI, SIGIR, WWW, IJCAI, COLING and KDD. A selected handful of her recent tutorials include:

- AAAI'22: Deep Learning on Graphs for Natural Language Processing. Language Processing.
- EMNLP'21: Knowledge-Enriched Natural Language Generation.
- ACL'21: Event-Centric Natural Language Processing.

Additional information is available at `https://blender.cs.illinois.edu/hengji.html`.

Ethical Considerations

Technological innovations often face the dual usage dilemma, in which the same advance may offer potential benefits and harms. For the news probing methodologies introduced in this tutorial, the distinction between beneficial use and harmful use depends mainly on the data and intention. Proper use of the technology requires that input corpora be legally and ethically obtained, with the target goal to fight misinformation and mal-intents. Besides, training and assessment data may be biased in ways that limit the system performance on less well-represented populations and in new domains – causing performance discrepancy for different ethnic, gender, and other sub-populations. Thus, questions concerning generalizability and fairness need to be carefully considered when applying news analysis techniques to specific settings. A general approach to ensure proper application of dual-use technology should incorporate ethical considerations as the first-order principles in every step of the system design, maintain transparency and interpretability of the data, algorithms, and models, and explore counter-measures to protect vulnerable groups.

References

Shruti Agarwal, Hany Farid, Yuming Gu, Mingming He, Koki Nagano, and Hao Li. 2019. Protecting world leaders against deep fakes. In *CVPR workshops*, volume 1.

Hunt Allcott and Matthew Gentzkow. 2017. Social media and fake news in the 2016 election. *Journal of economic perspectives*, 31(2):211–36.

Shivangi Aneja, Chris Bregler, and Matthias Nießner. 2021. Cosmos: Catching out-of-context misinformation with self-supervised learning. *arXiv preprint arXiv:2101.06278*.

Ramy Baly, Giovanni Da San Martino, James Glass, and Preslav Nakov. 2020. We can detect your bias: Predicting the political ideology of news articles. In *Proceedings of the 2020 Conference on Empirical Methods in Natural Language Processing*, EMNLP '20, pages 4982–4991.

Ramy Baly, Georgi Karadzhov, Dimitar Alexandrov, James Glass, and Preslav Nakov. 2018. Predicting factuality of reporting and bias of news media sources. In *Proceedings of the 2018 Conference on Empirical Methods in Natural Language Processing*, pages 3528–3539, Brussels, Belgium. Association for Computational Linguistics.

Nadia M Brashier, Gordon Pennycook, Adam J Berinsky, and David G Rand. 2021. Timing matters when correcting fake news. *Proceedings of the National Academy of Sciences*, 118(5).

Tom Buchanan. 2020. Why do people spread false information online? The effects of message and viewer characteristics on self-reported likelihood of sharing social media disinformation. *PLOS One*, 15(10):e0239666.

Ronit Chawla. 2019. Deepfakes: How a pervert shook the world. *International Journal of Advance Research and Development*, 4(6):4–8.

Lu Cheng, Ruocheng Guo, Kai Shu, and Huan Liu. 2021. Causal understanding of fake news dissemination on social media. In *Proceedings of the 27th ACM SIGKDD Conference on Knowledge Discovery & Data Mining*, pages 148–157.

Leshem Choshen, Dan Eldad, Daniel Hershcovich, Elior Sulem, and Omri Abend. 2019. The language of legal and illegal activity on the Darknet. In *Proceedings of the 57th Annual Meeting of the Association for Computational Linguistics*, ACL '19, pages 4271–4279, Florence, Italy.

Botambu Collins, Dinh Tuyen Hoang, Ngoc Thanh Nguyen, and Dosam Hwang. 2021. Trends in combating fake news on social media–a survey. *Journal of Information and Telecommunication*, 5(2):247–266.

Jeff Da, Maxwell Forbes, Rowan Zellers, Anthony Zheng, Jena D Hwang, Antoine Bosselut, and Yejin Choi. 2021. Edited media understanding frames: Reasoning about the intent and implications of visual misinformation. In *Proceedings of the 59th Annual Meeting of the Association for Computational Linguistics and the 11th International Joint Conference on Natural Language Processing*, ACL-IJNCLP '21, pages 2026–2039.

Leon Derczynski and Arkaitz Zubiaga. 2020. Detection and resolution of rumors and misinformation with nlp. In *Proceedings of the 28th International Conference on Computational Linguistics: Tutorial Abstracts*, pages 22–26.

Dimitar Dimitrov, Bishr Bin Ali, Shaden Shaar, Firoj Alam, Fabrizio Silvestri, Hamed Firooz, Preslav Nakov, and Giovanni Da San Martino. 2021. Detecting propaganda techniques in memes. In *Proceedings of the 59th Annual Meeting of the Association for Computational Linguistics and the 11th International Joint Conference on Natural Language Processing*, ACL-IJCNLP '21, pages 6603–6617.

Ullrich KH Ecker, Stephan Lewandowsky, John Cook, Philipp Schmid, Lisa K Fazio, Nadia Brashier, Panayiota Kendeou, Emily K Vraga, and Michelle A Amazeen. 2022. The psychological drivers of misinformation belief and its resistance to correction. *Nature Reviews Psychology*, 1(1):13–29.

Lisa Fan, Marshall White, Eva Sharma, Ruisi Su, Prafulla Kumar Choubey, Ruihong Huang, and Lu Wang. 2019. In plain sight: Media bias through the lens of factual reporting. In *Proceedings of the 2019 Conference on Empirical Methods in Natural Language Processing and the 9th International Joint Conference on Natural Language Processing*, EMNLP-IJCNLP '19, pages 6343–6349, Hong Kong, China.

Maxwell Forbes, Jena D. Hwang, Vered Shwartz, Maarten Sap, and Yejin Choi. 2020. Social chemistry 101: Learning to reason about social and moral norms. In *Proceedings of the 2020 Conference on Empirical Methods in Natural Language Processing*, EMNLP '20, pages 653–670.

Yi Fung, Christopher Thomas, Revanth Gangi Reddy, Sandeep Polisetty, Heng Ji, Shih-Fu Chang, Kathleen McKeown, Mohit Bansal, and Avirup Sil. 2021. InfoSurgeon: Cross-media fine-grained information consistency checking for fake news detection. In *Proceedings of the Annual Meeting of the Association for Computational Linguistics and the International Joint Conference on Natural Language Processing*, ACL-IJCNLP '21, pages 1683–1698.

Fantahun Gereme, William Zhu, Tewodros Ayall, and Dagmawi Alemu. 2021. Combating fake news in "low-resource" languages: Amharic fake news detection accompanied by resource crafting. *Information*, 12(1):20.

David Güera and Edward J Delp. 2018. Deepfake video detection using recurrent neural networks. In *2018 15th IEEE international conference on advanced video and signal based surveillance (AVSS)*, pages 1–6. IEEE.

Zhijiang Guo, Michael Schlichtkrull, and Andreas Vlachos. 2022. A survey on automated fact-checking. *Transactions of the Association for Computational Linguistics*, 10:178–206.

Linmei Hu, Tianchi Yang, Luhao Zhang, Wanjun Zhong, Duyu Tang, Chuan Shi, Nan Duan, and Ming Zhou. 2021. Compare to the knowledge: Graph neural fake news detection with external knowledge. In *Proceedings of the 59th Annual Meeting of the Association for Computational Linguistics and the 11th International Joint Conference on Natural Language Processing*, ACL-IJCNLP '21, pages 754–763.

Mingzhen Huang, Shan Jia, and Siwei Lyu. 2022. Text-Image De-Contextualization Detection Using Vision-Language Models. In *IEEE International Conference on Acoustics, Speech and Signal Processing (ICASSP)*, Singapore.

Hamid Karimi and Jiliang Tang. 2019. Learning hierarchical discourse-level structure for fake news detection. In *Proceedings of the 2019 Conference of the North American Chapter of the Association for Computational Linguistics: Human Language Technologies*, NAACL-HLT '19, pages 3432–3442, Minneapolis, MN, USA.

Vivek Kulkarni, Junting Ye, Steve Skiena, and William Yang Wang. 2018. Multi-view models for political ideology detection of news articles. In *Proceedings of the 2018 Conference on Empirical Methods in Natural Language Processing*, pages 3518–3527, Brussels, Belgium. Association for Computational Linguistics.

Nayeon Lee, Yejin Bang, Andrea Madotto, and Pascale Fung. 2021a. Mitigating media bias through neutral article generation. *arXiv preprint arXiv:2104.00336*.

Nayeon Lee, Belinda Z. Li, Sinong Wang, Pascale Fung, Hao Ma, Wen-tau Yih, and Madian Khabsa. 2021b. On unifying misinformation detection. In *Proceedings of the 2021 Conference of the North American Chapter of the Association for Computational Linguistics: Human Language Technologies*, NAACL-HLT '21, pages 5479–5485.

Lihui Liu, Boxin Du, Yi Ren Fung, Heng Ji, Jiejun Xu, and Hanghang Tong. 2021. Kompare: A knowledge graph comparative reasoning system. In *Proceedings of the 27th ACM SIGKDD Conference on Knowledge Discovery Data Mining*, KDD '21, page 3308–3318, New York, NY, USA. Association for Computing Machinery.

Yi-Ju Lu and Cheng-Te Li. 2020. GCAN: Graph-aware co-attention networks for explainable fake news detection on social media. In *Proceedings of the 58th Annual Meeting of the Association for Computational Linguistics*, pages 505–514, Online. Association for Computational Linguistics.

Ahmadreza Mosallanezhad, Kai Shu, and Huan Liu. 2021. Generating topic-preserving synthetic news. In *2021 IEEE International Conference on Big Data (Big Data)*, pages 490–499.

Taichi Murayama, Shoko Wakamiya, and Eiji Aramaki. 2021. Mitigation of diachronic bias in fake news detection dataset. In *Proceedings of the Seventh Workshop on Noisy User-generated Text*, W-NUT '21, pages 182–188.

Preslav Nakov and Giovanni Da San Martino. 2020. Fact-checking, fake news, propaganda, and media bias: Truth seeking in the post-truth era. In *Proceedings of the 2020 Conference on Empirical Methods in Natural Language Processing: Tutorial Abstracts*, pages 7–19.

Gordon Pennycook and David G Rand. 2021. The psychology of fake news. *Trends in cognitive sciences*, 25(5):388–402.

Verónica Pérez-Rosas, Bennett Kleinberg, Alexandra Lefevre, and Rada Mihalcea. 2018. Automatic detection of fake news. In *Proceedings of the 27th International Conference on Computational Linguistics*, COLING '18, pages 3391–3401, Santa Fe, NM, USA.

Shraman Pramanick, Shivam Sharma, Dimitar Dimitrov, Md. Shad Akhtar, Preslav Nakov, and Tanmoy Chakraborty. 2021. MOMENTA: A multimodal framework for detecting harmful memes and their targets. In *Findings of the Association for Computational Linguistics: EMNLP 2021*, pages 4439–4455, Punta Cana, Dominican Republic.

Kenneth Rapoza. Can 'fake news' impact the stock market? *Forbes*.

Hannah Rashkin, Eunsol Choi, Jin Yea Jang, Svitlana Volkova, and Yejin Choi. 2017. Truth of varying shades: Analyzing language in fake news and political fact-checking. In *Proceedings of the 2017 conference on empirical methods in natural language processing*, pages 2931–2937.

Victoria L Rubin, Yimin Chen, and Nadia K Conroy. 2015. Deception detection for news: three types of fakes. *Proceedings of the Association for Information Science and Technology*, 52(1):1–4.

Estela Saquete, David Tomás, Paloma Moreda, Patricio Martínez-Barco, and Manuel Palomar. 2020. Fighting post-truth using natural language processing: A review and open challenges. *Expert systems with applications*, 141:112943.

Tal Schuster, Roei Schuster, Darsh J Shah, and Regina Barzilay. 2020. The limitations of stylometry for detecting machine-generated fake news. *Computational Linguistics*, 46(2):499–510.

Shaden Shaar, Nikolay Babulkov, Giovanni Da San Martino, and Preslav Nakov. 2020. That is a known lie: Detecting previously fact-checked claims. In *Proceedings of the 58th Annual Meeting of the Association for Computational Linguistics*, ACL '20, pages 3607–3618.

Kai Shu, Limeng Cui, Suhang Wang, Dongwon Lee, and Huan Liu. 2019. dEFEND: Explainable fake news detection. In *Proceedings of the 25th International Conference on Knowledge Discovery & Data Mining*, KDD '19, pages 395–405, Anchorage, AK, USA.

Kai Shu, Yichuan Li, Kaize Ding, and Huan Liu. 2021. Fact-enhanced synthetic news generation. *Proceedings of the AAAI Conference on Artificial Intelligence*, 35(15):13825–13833.

Kai Shu, Deepak Mahudeswaran, Suhang Wang, and Huan Liu. 2020. Hierarchical propagation networks for fake news detection: Investigation and exploitation. In *Proceedings of the International AAAI Conference on Web and Social Media*, volume 14, pages 626–637.

Daniel H Solomon, Richard Bucala, Mariana J Kaplan, and Peter A Nigrovic. 2020. The "infodemic" of covid-19.

Reuben Tan, Bryan Plummer, and Kate Saenko. 2020. Detecting cross-modal inconsistency to defend against neural fake news. In *Proceedings of the 2020 Conference on Empirical Methods in Natural Language Processing*, EMNLP '20, pages 2081–2106.

Kehan Wang, David Chan, Seth Z Zhao, John Canny, and Avideh Zakhor. 2022. Misinformation detection in social media video posts. *arXiv preprint arXiv:2202.07706*.

Claire Wardle, Hossein Derakhshan, et al. 2018. Thinking about 'information disorder': formats of misinformation, disinformation, and mal-information. *Ireton, Cherilyn; Posetti, Julie. Journalism,'fake news'& disinformation. Paris: Unesco*, pages 43–54.

Xueqing Wu, Kung-Hsiang Huang, Yi Fung, and Heng Ji. 2022. Cross-document misinformation detection based on event graph reasoning. In *NAACL 2022*, Seattle, WA, USA.

Rowan Zellers, Ari Holtzman, Hannah Rashkin, Yonatan Bisk, Ali Farhadi, Franziska Roesner, and Yejin Choi. 2019. Defending against neural fake news. *Advances in neural information processing systems*, 32.

Xichen Zhang and Ali A Ghorbani. 2020. An overview of online fake news: Characterization, detection, and discussion. *Information Processing & Management*, 57(2):102025.

Kaimin Zhou, Chang Shu, Binyang Li, and Jey Han Lau. 2019. Early rumour detection. In *Proceedings of the 2019 Conference of the North American Chapter of the Association for Computational Linguistics: Human Language Technologies*, NAACL-HLT '19, pages 1614–1623, Minneapolis, MN, USA.

A Tour of Explicit Multilingual Semantics: Word Sense Disambiguation, Semantic Role Labeling and Semantic Parsing

Roberto Navigli, Edoardo Barba, Simone Conia
Sapienza NLP Group
Sapienza University of Rome
first.lastname@uniroma1.it

Rexhina Blloshmi*
Amazon Alexa AI
Berlin, Germany
blloshmi@amazon.de

Abstract

The recent advent of modern pretrained language models has sparked a revolution in Natural Language Processing (NLP), especially in multilingual and cross-lingual applications. Today, such language models have become the *de facto* standard for providing rich input representations to neural systems, achieving unprecedented results in an increasing range of benchmarks. However, questions that often arise are: firstly, whether current language models are, indeed, able to capture explicit, symbolic meaning; secondly, if they are, to what extent; thirdly, and perhaps more importantly, whether current approaches are capable of scaling across languages.

In this cutting-edge tutorial, we will review recent efforts that have aimed at shedding light on meaning in NLP, with a focus on three key open problems in lexical and sentence-level semantics: Word Sense Disambiguation, Semantic Role Labeling, and Semantic Parsing. After a brief introduction, we will spotlight how state-of-the-art models tackle these tasks in multiple languages, showing where they excel and where they fail. We hope that this tutorial will broaden the audience interested in multilingual semantics and inspire researchers to further advance the field.

1 Tutorial Description and Relevance

Over the past few years, the field of Natural Language Processing (NLP) has witnessed tremendous growth, mainly thanks to the increasingly wide availability of modern pretrained language models, such as ELMo (Peters et al., 2018), BERT (Devlin et al., 2019), and BART (Lewis et al., 2020), which have enabled unprecedented results in a broad range of tasks, from Neural Machine Translation to Question Answering, Information Retrieval and Text Summarization, *inter alia*. However, important questions that naturally arise when looking at the recent impressive gains in the field are whether such powerful language models learn to encode *semantic knowledge* and, if they are, to what extent. More importantly, the escalating interest in multilingual NLP demands approaches that are able to identify and transfer semantics across a multitude of languages, especially those for which there is a scarce amount of data available.

In this tutorial, we will review recent studies in lexical and sentence semantics, paying special attention to state-of-the-art approaches and how they tackle multilinguality in three fundamental tasks for Natural Language Understanding (NLU): Word Sense Disambiguation (WSD), Semantic Role Labeling (SRL) and Semantic Parsing (SP). In addition to an introduction to multilingual NLU, for each task we will provide, i) a gentle introduction, ii) an overview of the inventories and resources most commonly adopted, iii) an outline of current approaches with a particular focus on multilinguality and cross-linguality in order to understand their strengths and shortcomings, and also pointing to promising directions for future work. Although there have been previous tutorials on Semantics in NLP, especially on SP (Lopez and Gilroy, 2018; Gardner et al., 2018; Koller et al., 2019), our tutorial will, instead, focus on the challenges of multilinguality and cross-linguality and how recent approaches based on pretrained language models tackle them.

Despite the increasing performance of huge language models in NLU tasks, recent studies have demonstrated that the integration of explicit semantics into deep learning techniques is beneficial not only in terms of performances (Levine et al., 2020), but also interpretability (Wiedemann et al., 2019) and cross-lingual transfer (Blloshmi et al., 2020).

2 Tutorial Structure and Contents

The tutorial will be structured in a bottom-up fashion: participants will be introduced to multilingual

*Proposal written while at Sapienza University of Rome.

Proceedings of the 2nd Conference of the Asia-Pacific Chapter of the Association for Computational Linguistics and the 12th International Joint Conference on Natural Language Processing: Tutorial Abstracts, pages 35–43

semantics, first at the lexical level with WSD, and then at the sentence level with SRL and SP, highlighting the most effective approaches to date, but also their weaknesses and future directions to address these.

2.1 Word Sense Disambiguation (WSD)

The tutorial will start with WSD as the lowest level of semantic abstraction. Its objective is to assign the most appropriate sense to a word in context from a finite set of possible choices (Navigli, 2009), which usually come from predefined sense inventories. Although, at a first glance, WSD may seem a simple task to a human, it has proven to be extremely challenging for machines. Indeed, depending on the sense inventory of choice, different linguistic phenomena may make the task difficult to tackle with standard classification techniques. Nonetheless, being able to link raw text to knowledge bases is fundamental in NLP (McCoy et al., 2019; Bender and Koller, 2020), bringing benefits in several fields, such as Machine Translation (Liu et al., 2018; Pu et al., 2018; Campolungo et al., 2022), Information Extraction (Delli Bovi et al., 2015), and Information Retrieval (Blloshmi et al., 2021b). We will start with an introduction to the task, presenting its most common formulation along with the challenges it poses. Then, we will describe state-of-the-art systems, highlighting their core contributions. Finally, we will conclude by presenting open challenges in multilingual WSD.

Resources for WSD. We will first present the standard resources currently in use for WSD, starting with WordNet (Miller et al., 1990), i.e., the most widely used sense inventory, and Open Multilingual Wordnet (Bond, 2011) and BabelNet (Navigli and Ponzetto, 2012; Navigli et al., 2021), two multilingual extensions of WordNet.

Current approaches in WSD. After the initial success of purely data-driven neural models in WSD (Yuan et al., 2016), subsequent approaches started to leverage information coming from knowledge bases in addition to standard training datasets (Huang et al., 2019; Bevilacqua and Navigli, 2020). We will put a special focus on state-of-the-art systems that rely on relational knowledge (Bevilacqua and Navigli, 2020) and sense definitions as additional knowledge (Blevins and Zettlemoyer, 2020; Barba et al., 2021a,b). We will explain how these approaches are data-efficient and why they are important, especially for low-resource languages.

2.2 Semantic Role Labeling (SRL)

While WSD is concerned with lexical-level meaning, SRL (Gildea and Jurafsky, 2000) investigates sentence-level semantics and is usually described informally as the task of automatically answering the question *"Who did What to Whom, Where, When, and How?"* (Màrquez et al., 2008). More precisely, its objective is to extract the predicate-argument structure of a sentence and, therefore, it is considered by some as a form of shallow Semantic Parsing. Over the years, SRL has been proven to be beneficial in several tasks, such as Question Answering (Shen and Lapata, 2007), Machine Translation (Marcheggiani et al., 2018), Video Understanding (Sadhu et al., 2021), and data augmentation (Ross et al., 2022). Following a general introduction to SRL, the tutorial will highlight some key details about the most popular predicate-argument structure inventories for SRL, the salient characteristics of current state-of-the-art systems, and why everything becomes more complex when trying to tackle multilingual and cross-lingual SRL.

Inventories for SRL. The tutorial will overview the main challenges that current predicate-argument structure inventories pose for multilingual and cross-lingual SRL, with particular focus on PropBank-style inventories (Palmer et al., 2005; Xue, 2008; Jindal et al., 2022), FrameNet (Baker et al., 1998) and VerbAtlas (Di Fabio et al., 2019).

Current approaches in SRL. Given its close ties with syntax, over the years one of the main distinctions between proposed approaches is whether they have chosen to rely on syntactic features (He et al., 2019; Marcheggiani and Titov, 2020; Conia and Navigli, 2020), or not (Marcheggiani et al., 2017; Cai et al., 2018). The tutorial will briefly cover the advantages and disadvantages of relying on syntax in multilingual SRL, but also highlight annotation projection techniques for cross-lingual SRL (Akbik et al., 2015; Daza and Frank, 2020), and how recent trends in multi-task learning (Conia et al., 2021) and generation (Blloshmi et al., 2021a; Paolini et al., 2021; Conia et al., 2022) are going beyond traditional approaches, hinting at new directions in SRL.

2.3 Semantic Parsing (SP)

Finally, the tutorial will bring participants to a higher level of semantic abstraction: SP, indeed, may be seen as "the task of mapping natural language sentences into *complete formal meaning representations* which a computer can execute" (Kate and Wong, 2010). Here we focus on formalisms that aim at encoding text in an abstract form that captures aspects of meaning – as opposed to executable formalisms for SP – that can be reusable in various scenarios, thus being domain independent. Indeed, SP formalisms have been successfully integrated into numerous downstream applications, such as Machine Translation (Song et al., 2019), Text Summarization (Hardy and Vlachos, 2018), Human-Robot Interaction (Bonial et al., 2020) and Question Answering (Kapanipathi et al., 2021). Nevertheless, research in SP has mainly focused on English, with only a handful of attempts in other languages.

Formalisms for SP. Over the years, various different formalisms have been proposed to encode semantic structures. We will first overview the most popular formalisms, such as Elementary Dependency Structures (Oepen and Lønning, 2006, EDS), Prague Tectogrammatical Graphs (Hajič et al., 2012, PTG), Universal Conceptual Cognitive Annotation (Abend and Rappoport, 2013, UCCA), Universal Decompositional Semantics (White et al., 2016, UDS), with a main focus on Abstract Meaning Representation (Banarescu et al., 2013) and BabelNet Meaning Representation, its fully-semantic extension (Martínez Lorenzo et al., 2022).

Current approaches in SP. SP is receiving ever growing attention that has led to numerous approaches of different flavors. Indeed, the advantages and disadvantages of parser types are variable across different formalisms. We will focus on two categories of approaches: *graph-based* ones (Zhang et al., 2019; Cai and Lam, 2020), that consist of transducing natural utterances into graphs, and *sequence-to-sequence* ones, that produce linearized graph structures for a given input text (Ge et al., 2019; Bevilacqua et al., 2021a). Due to the recent development of encoder-decoder pretrained architectures, sequence-to-sequence approaches to SP are emerging as the best-performing methods, not only in English (Bevilacqua et al., 2021a), but also in other languages (Procopio et al., 2021b).

3 Type, Prerequisites and Audience

This is a **cutting-edge tutorial**. State-of-the-art approaches for three key areas of multilingual lexical and sentence semantics will be presented, and some of them will be discussed in detail. We expect **80-120 attendees** from different fields as the barriers to entry will be low:

- **Math prerequisites:** Linear algebra, e.g., matrix operations, linear/non-linear functions.
- **Machine Learning prerequisites:** General concepts of classification, e.g., token classification, sequence labeling, sequence-to-sequence.
- **NLP prerequisites:** High-level notions about pretrained language models.

4 Reading List

Recommended work to read before the tutorial:

- Bevilacqua et al. (2021b): a survey on recent trends in **WSD**;
- Blevins and Zettlemoyer (2020) and Barba et al. (2021a): two recent **WSD** systems that take advantage of sense definitions;
- Màrquez et al. (2008) and Hajic et al. (2009): an introduction to **SRL** and the largest gold benchmark for multilingual **SRL**;
- He et al. (2019) and Conia et al. (2021): two recent approaches to multilingual **SRL**, a syntax-aware and a syntax-agnostic one;
- Koller et al. (2019) and Oepen et al. (2020): tutorial on recent work and shared task on **SP**;
- Banarescu et al. (2013) and Bevilacqua et al. (2021a): the introduction to the AMR formalism for **SP** and a state-of-the-art system for AMR parsing and generation;

5 Tutorial Outline (3h)

Part 0: Introduction (10 minutes). Introduction, motivation, goals, how the tutorial is organized.

Part 1: WSD (40 minutes)

- Introduction to WSD, formulation, examples;
- Sense inventories for WSD: WordNet, Open Multilingual WordNet and BabelNet;
- Current approaches in multilingual WSD: purely data-driven vs. knowledge-enhanced supervision; going beyond sense inventories.

QA & Break (10 minutes)

Part 2: SRL (40 minutes)

- Introduction to SRL, formulation, examples;
- Predicate-argument structure inventories: the case of multilingual and cross-lingual SRL;
- Current approaches in multilingual and cross-lingual SRL: syntax-aware vs syntax-agnostic systems, annotation projection techniques, and novel directions.

QA & Break (10 minutes)

Part 3: SP (40 minutes)

- Introduction to SP, formulation, examples;
- Main formalisms for SP;
- Current approaches in cross-lingual SP: annotation projection, data augmentation via translation, generation.

QA & Break (10 minutes)

Part 4: Conclusion (20 minutes). Where to go from here, general considerations, a look to the future of explicit lexical and sentence semantics.

6 Pedagogical Material

Part 1 (WSD), Part 2 (SRL) and Part 3 (SP) will include brief hands-on sessions. These will be supported by interactive demos and Jupyter/iPython/Colab notebooks to invite participants to play with high-performance pretrained systems for WSD, SRL and SP. All material (slides, notebooks, pretrained models) will be freely available online to let discussions continue beyond the tutorial and for teaching purposes.

7 Presenters

Roberto Navigli is a Full Professor in the Department of Computer, Control and Management Engineering (DIAG) of Sapienza University of Rome, from which he also obtained his Ph.D. in Computer Science in 2007. At Sapienza he has taught courses for 4 Master's programmes (CS, CS Engineering, AI & Robotics and Data Science), including NLP. He has been a keynote speaker at more than 30 **conferences** and **workshops**, including IJCNLP, IJCAI-ECAI (early career spotlight), AMLD, SwissText+KONVENS, CLNLP, RANLP, TALN, eLex. In 2014, he co-presented a (pre-neural) tutorial on "Multilingual WSD and Entity Linking" at COLING. In 2016, he co-presented a tutorial on "Semantic Representations of Word Senses and Concepts" at ACL. He has worked and published with around **200 researchers** from all over the world in more than 200 papers in the area of NLP with a particular focus on **Natural Language Understanding** and **multilinguality**, attracting 18,000+ citations.

Rexhina Blloshmi is a Machine Learning Scientist at Amazon Alexa AI in Berlin. Her PhD focused on Semantic Parsing. She contributed in this field with several publications in AI and NLP conferences (3 EMNLP, 1 IJCAI and 3 AAAI), mainly on English and Cross-Lingual Abstract Meaning Representation and Semantic Role Labeling, but also on novel formalisms such as BabelNet Meaning Representation.

Edoardo Barba is a third-year PhD Student in NLP at Sapienza University of Rome. His research is mostly focused on Word Sense Disambiguation. He contributed to several articles regarding both state-of-the-art and data efficient systems for WSD (Barba et al., 2021a) as well as Data Augmentation techniques for Multilingual WSD (Barba et al., 2020; Procopio et al., 2021a). Teaching Assistant in 2020 and 2021 for the NLP course at Sapienza (taught in English).

Simone Conia is a third-year PhD Student in NLP at Sapienza University of Rome. His research revolves around multilingual and cross-lingual semantics, with numerous papers on WSD and SRL published at *ACL and other top-tier conferences. Simone is recipient of an **Outstanding Paper Award at NAACL-2021** for his work on cross-lingual SRL. Teaching Assistant in 2020 and 2021 for the NLP course at Sapienza (taught in English).

8 Ethics & Diversity Statement

We do not foresee any major ethical issue for the topics covered in this tutorial. We acknowledge that pretrained language models may show biases towards some stereotypes, cultures, ethnic and/or social groups: perpetrating such biases is not in our intentions. We will cover a variety of languages, including Arabic, Chinese, English, French, German, Italian, Spanish: we hope that our effort can promote new studies aimed at making lexical and sentence semantics increasingly more inclusive of lower-resource languages.

References

Omri Abend and Ari Rappoport. 2013. Universal Conceptual Cognitive Annotation (UCCA). In *Proceedings of the 51st Annual Meeting of the Association for Computational Linguistics (Volume 1: Long Papers)*, pages 228–238, Sofia, Bulgaria. Association for Computational Linguistics.

Alan Akbik, Laura Chiticariu, Marina Danilevsky, Yunyao Li, Shivakumar Vaithyanathan, and Huaiyu Zhu. 2015. Generating high quality proposition Banks for multilingual semantic role labeling. In *Proceedings of the 53rd Annual Meeting of the Association for Computational Linguistics and the 7th International Joint Conference on Natural Language Processing (Volume 1: Long Papers)*, pages 397–407, Beijing, China. Association for Computational Linguistics.

Collin F. Baker, Charles J. Fillmore, and John B. Lowe. 1998. The Berkeley FrameNet project. In *36th Annual Meeting of the Association for Computational Linguistics and 17th International Conference on Computational Linguistics, Volume 1*, pages 86–90, Montreal, Quebec, Canada. Association for Computational Linguistics.

Laura Banarescu, Claire Bonial, Shu Cai, Madalina Georgescu, Kira Griffitt, Ulf Hermjakob, Kevin Knight, Philipp Koehn, Martha Palmer, and Nathan Schneider. 2013. Abstract Meaning Representation for sembanking. In *Proceedings of the 7th Linguistic Annotation Workshop and Interoperability with Discourse*, pages 178–186, Sofia, Bulgaria. Association for Computational Linguistics.

Edoardo Barba, Tommaso Pasini, and Roberto Navigli. 2021a. ESC: Redesigning WSD with extractive sense comprehension. In *Proceedings of the 2021 Conference of the North American Chapter of the Association for Computational Linguistics: Human Language Technologies*, pages 4661–4672, Online. Association for Computational Linguistics.

Edoardo Barba, Luigi Procopio, Niccolò Campolungo, Tommaso Pasini, and Roberto Navigli. 2020. Mulan: Multilingual label propagation for word sense disambiguation. In *Proceedings of the Twenty-Ninth International Joint Conference on Artificial Intelligence, IJCAI-20*, pages 3837–3844. International Joint Conferences on Artificial Intelligence Organization. Main track.

Edoardo Barba, Luigi Procopio, and Roberto Navigli. 2021b. ConSeC: Word sense disambiguation as continuous sense comprehension. In *Proceedings of the 2021 Conference on Empirical Methods in Natural Language Processing*, pages 1492–1503, Online and Punta Cana, Dominican Republic. Association for Computational Linguistics.

Emily M. Bender and Alexander Koller. 2020. Climbing towards NLU: On meaning, form, and understanding in the age of data. In *Proceedings of the 58th Annual Meeting of the Association for Computational Linguistics*, pages 5185–5198, Online. Association for Computational Linguistics.

Michele Bevilacqua, Rexhina Blloshmi, and Roberto Navigli. 2021a. One SPRING to Rule Them Both: Symmetric AMR Semantic Parsing and Generation without a Complex Pipeline. *Proceedings of the AAAI Conference on Artificial Intelligence*, 35(14):12564–12573.

Michele Bevilacqua and Roberto Navigli. 2020. Breaking through the 80% glass ceiling: Raising the state of the art in word sense disambiguation by incorporating knowledge graph information. In *Proceedings of the 58th Annual Meeting of the Association for Computational Linguistics*, pages 2854–2864, Online. Association for Computational Linguistics.

Michele Bevilacqua, Tommaso Pasini, Alessandro Raganato, and Roberto Navigli. 2021b. Recent trends in word sense disambiguation: A survey. In *Proceedings of the Thirtieth International Joint Conference on Artificial Intelligence, IJCAI 2021, Virtual Event / Montreal, Canada, 19-27 August 2021*, pages 4330–4338. ijcai.org.

Terra Blevins and Luke Zettlemoyer. 2020. Moving down the long tail of word sense disambiguation with gloss informed bi-encoders. In *Proceedings of the 58th Annual Meeting of the Association for Computational Linguistics*, pages 1006–1017, Online. Association for Computational Linguistics.

Rexhina Blloshmi, Simone Conia, Rocco Tripodi, and Roberto Navigli. 2021a. Generating senses and roles: An end-to-end model for dependency- and span-based semantic role labeling. In *Proceedings of the Thirtieth International Joint Conference on Artificial Intelligence, IJCAI-21*, pages 3786–3793. International Joint Conferences on Artificial Intelligence Organization. Main Track.

Rexhina Blloshmi, Tommaso Pasini, Niccolò Campolungo, Somnath Banerjee, Roberto Navigli, and Gabriella Pasi. 2021b. IR like a SIR: Sense-enhanced Information Retrieval for Multiple Languages. In *Proceedings of the 2021 Conference on Empirical Methods in Natural Language Processing*, pages 1030–1041, Online and Punta Cana, Dominican Republic. Association for Computational Linguistics.

Rexhina Blloshmi, Rocco Tripodi, and Roberto Navigli. 2020. XL-AMR: Enabling cross-lingual AMR parsing with transfer learning techniques. In *Proceedings of the 2020 Conference on Empirical Methods in Natural Language Processing (EMNLP)*, pages 2487–2500, Online. Association for Computational Linguistics.

Francis Bond. 2011. A survey of wordnets and their licenses.

Claire Bonial, Lucia Donatelli, Mitchell Abrams, Stephanie M. Lukin, Stephen Tratz, Matthew Marge,

Ron Artstein, David Traum, and Clare Voss. 2020. Dialogue-AMR: Abstract Meaning Representation for dialogue. In *Proceedings of the 12th Language Resources and Evaluation Conference*, pages 684–695, Marseille, France. European Language Resources Association.

Deng Cai and Wai Lam. 2020. AMR parsing via graph-sequence iterative inference. In *Proceedings of the 58th Annual Meeting of the Association for Computational Linguistics*, pages 1290–1301, Online. Association for Computational Linguistics.

Jiaxun Cai, Shexia He, Zuchao Li, and Hai Zhao. 2018. A full end-to-end semantic role labeler, syntactic-agnostic over syntactic-aware? In *Proceedings of the 27th International Conference on Computational Linguistics*, pages 2753–2765, Santa Fe, New Mexico, USA. Association for Computational Linguistics.

Niccolò Campolungo, Federico Martelli, Francesco Saina, and Roberto Navigli. 2022. DiBiMT: A novel benchmark for measuring Word Sense Disambiguation biases in Machine Translation. In *Proceedings of the 60th Annual Meeting of the Association for Computational Linguistics (Volume 1: Long Papers)*, pages 4331–4352, Dublin, Ireland. Association for Computational Linguistics.

Simone Conia, Andrea Bacciu, and Roberto Navigli. 2021. Unifying cross-lingual semantic role labeling with heterogeneous linguistic resources. In *Proceedings of the 2021 Conference of the North American Chapter of the Association for Computational Linguistics: Human Language Technologies*, pages 338–351, Online. Association for Computational Linguistics.

Simone Conia, Edoardo Barba, Alessandro Scirè, and Roberto Navigli. 2022. Semantic Role Labeling meets definition modeling: Using natural language to describe predicate-argument structures. In *Findings of the Association for Computational Linguistics: EMNLP 2022*. Association for Computational Linguistics.

Simone Conia and Roberto Navigli. 2020. Bridging the gap in multilingual semantic role labeling: a language-agnostic approach. In *Proceedings of the 28th International Conference on Computational Linguistics*, pages 1396–1410, Barcelona, Spain (Online). International Committee on Computational Linguistics.

Angel Daza and Anette Frank. 2020. X-SRL: A parallel cross-lingual semantic role labeling dataset. In *Proceedings of the 2020 Conference on Empirical Methods in Natural Language Processing (EMNLP)*, pages 3904–3914, Online. Association for Computational Linguistics.

Claudio Delli Bovi, Luca Telesca, and Roberto Navigli. 2015. Large-scale information extraction from textual definitions through deep syntactic and semantic analysis. *Transactions of the Association for Computational Linguistics*, 3:529–543.

Jacob Devlin, Ming-Wei Chang, Kenton Lee, and Kristina Toutanova. 2019. BERT: Pre-training of deep bidirectional transformers for language understanding. In *Proceedings of the 2019 Conference of the North American Chapter of the Association for Computational Linguistics: Human Language Technologies, Volume 1 (Long and Short Papers)*, pages 4171–4186, Minneapolis, Minnesota. Association for Computational Linguistics.

Andrea Di Fabio, Simone Conia, and Roberto Navigli. 2019. VerbAtlas: a novel large-scale verbal semantic resource and its application to semantic role labeling. In *Proceedings of the 2019 Conference on Empirical Methods in Natural Language Processing and the 9th International Joint Conference on Natural Language Processing (EMNLP-IJCNLP)*, pages 627–637, Hong Kong, China. Association for Computational Linguistics.

Matt Gardner, Pradeep Dasigi, Srinivasan Iyer, Alane Suhr, and Luke Zettlemoyer. 2018. Neural semantic parsing. In *Proceedings of the 56th Annual Meeting of the Association for Computational Linguistics: Tutorial Abstracts*, pages 17–18, Melbourne, Australia. Association for Computational Linguistics.

DongLai Ge, Junhui Li, Muhua Zhu, and Shoushan Li. 2019. Modeling source syntax and semantics for neural amr parsing. In *Proceedings of the Twenty-Eighth International Joint Conference on Artificial Intelligence, IJCAI-19*, pages 4975–4981. International Joint Conferences on Artificial Intelligence Organization.

Daniel Gildea and Daniel Jurafsky. 2000. Automatic labeling of semantic roles. In *Proceedings of the 38th Annual Meeting of the Association for Computational Linguistics*, pages 512–520, Hong Kong. Association for Computational Linguistics.

Jan Hajic, Massimiliano Ciaramita, Richard Johansson, Daisuke Kawahara, Maria Antònia Martí, Lluís Màrquez, Adam Meyers, Joakim Nivre, Sebastian Padó, Jan Stepánek, Pavel Stranák, Mihai Surdeanu, Nianwen Xue, and Yi Zhang. 2009. The conll-2009 shared task: Syntactic and semantic dependencies in multiple languages. In *Proceedings of the Thirteenth Conference on Computational Natural Language Learning: Shared Task, CoNLL 2009, Boulder, Colorado, USA, June 4, 2009*, pages 1–18. ACL.

Jan Hajič, Eva Hajičová, Jarmila Panevová, Petr Sgall, Ondřej Bojar, Silvie Cinková, Eva Fučíková, Marie Mikulová, Petr Pajas, Jan Popelka, Jiří Semecký, Jana Šindlerová, Jan Štěpánek, Josef Toman, Zdeňka Urešová, and Zdeněk Žabokrtský. 2012. Announcing Prague Czech-English Dependency Treebank 2.0. In *Proceedings of the Eighth International Conference on Language Resources and Evaluation (LREC'12)*, pages 3153–3160, Istanbul, Turkey. European Language Resources Association (ELRA).

Hardy Hardy and Andreas Vlachos. 2018. Guided neural language generation for abstractive summarization using Abstract Meaning Representation. In *Proceedings of the 2018 Conference on Empirical Methods in Natural Language Processing*, pages 768–773, Brussels, Belgium. Association for Computational Linguistics.

Shexia He, Zuchao Li, and Hai Zhao. 2019. Syntax-aware multilingual semantic role labeling. In *Proceedings of the 2019 Conference on Empirical Methods in Natural Language Processing and the 9th International Joint Conference on Natural Language Processing (EMNLP-IJCNLP)*, pages 5350–5359, Hong Kong, China. Association for Computational Linguistics.

Luyao Huang, Chi Sun, Xipeng Qiu, and Xuanjing Huang. 2019. GlossBERT: BERT for word sense disambiguation with gloss knowledge. In *Proceedings of the 2019 Conference on Empirical Methods in Natural Language Processing and the 9th International Joint Conference on Natural Language Processing (EMNLP-IJCNLP)*, pages 3509–3514, Hong Kong, China. Association for Computational Linguistics.

Ishan Jindal, Alexandre Rademaker, Michał Ulewicz, Ha Linh, Huyen Nguyen, Khoi-Nguyen Tran, Huaiyu Zhu, and Yunyao Li. 2022. Universal proposition bank 2.0. In *Proceedings of the Language Resources and Evaluation Conference*, pages 1700–1711, Marseille, France. European Language Resources Association.

Pavan Kapanipathi, Ibrahim Abdelaziz, Srinivas Ravishankar, Salim Roukos, Alexander Gray, Ramón Fernandez Astudillo, Maria Chang, Cristina Cornelio, Saswati Dana, Achille Fokoue, Dinesh Garg, Alfio Gliozzo, Sairam Gurajada, Hima Karanam, Naweed Khan, Dinesh Khandelwal, Young-Suk Lee, Yunyao Li, Francois Luus, Ndivhuwo Makondo, Nandana Mihindukulasooriya, Tahira Naseem, Sumit Neelam, Lucian Popa, Revanth Gangi Reddy, Ryan Riegel, Gaetano Rossiello, Udit Sharma, G P Shrivatsa Bhargav, and Mo Yu. 2021. Leveraging Abstract Meaning Representation for knowledge base question answering. In *Findings of the Association for Computational Linguistics: ACL-IJCNLP 2021*, pages 3884–3894, Online. Association for Computational Linguistics.

Rohit J. Kate and Yuk Wah Wong. 2010. Semantic parsing: The task, the state of the art and the future. In *Proceedings of the 48th Annual Meeting of the Association for Computational Linguistics: Tutorial Abstracts*, page 6, Uppsala, Sweden. Association for Computational Linguistics.

Alexander Koller, Stephan Oepen, and Weiwei Sun. 2019. Graph-based meaning representations: Design and processing. In *Proceedings of the 57th Annual Meeting of the Association for Computational Linguistics: Tutorial Abstracts*, pages 6–11, Florence, Italy. Association for Computational Linguistics.

Yoav Levine, Barak Lenz, Or Dagan, Ori Ram, Dan Padnos, Or Sharir, Shai Shalev-Shwartz, Amnon Shashua, and Yoav Shoham. 2020. SenseBERT: Driving some sense into BERT. In *Proceedings of the 58th Annual Meeting of the Association for Computational Linguistics*, pages 4656–4667, Online. Association for Computational Linguistics.

Mike Lewis, Yinhan Liu, Naman Goyal, Marjan Ghazvininejad, Abdelrahman Mohamed, Omer Levy, Veselin Stoyanov, and Luke Zettlemoyer. 2020. BART: Denoising sequence-to-sequence pre-training for natural language generation, translation, and comprehension. In *Proceedings of the 58th Annual Meeting of the Association for Computational Linguistics*, pages 7871–7880, Online. Association for Computational Linguistics.

Frederick Liu, Han Lu, and Graham Neubig. 2018. Handling homographs in neural machine translation. In *Proceedings of the 2018 Conference of the North American Chapter of the Association for Computational Linguistics: Human Language Technologies, Volume 1 (Long Papers)*, pages 1336–1345, New Orleans, Louisiana. Association for Computational Linguistics.

Adam Lopez and Sorcha Gilroy. 2018. Graph formalisms for meaning representations. In *Proceedings of the 2018 Conference on Empirical Methods in Natural Language Processing: Tutorial Abstracts*, Melbourne, Australia. Association for Computational Linguistics.

Diego Marcheggiani, Jasmijn Bastings, and Ivan Titov. 2018. Exploiting semantics in neural machine translation with graph convolutional networks. In *Proceedings of the 2018 Conference of the North American Chapter of the Association for Computational Linguistics: Human Language Technologies, Volume 2 (Short Papers)*, pages 486–492, New Orleans, Louisiana. Association for Computational Linguistics.

Diego Marcheggiani, Anton Frolov, and Ivan Titov. 2017. A simple and accurate syntax-agnostic neural model for dependency-based semantic role labeling. In *Proceedings of the 21st Conference on Computational Natural Language Learning (CoNLL 2017)*, pages 411–420, Vancouver, Canada. Association for Computational Linguistics.

Diego Marcheggiani and Ivan Titov. 2020. Graph convolutions over constituent trees for syntax-aware semantic role labeling. In *Proceedings of the 2020 Conference on Empirical Methods in Natural Language Processing (EMNLP)*, pages 3915–3928, Online. Association for Computational Linguistics.

Lluís Màrquez, Xavier Carreras, Kenneth C. Litkowski, and Suzanne Stevenson. 2008. Special issue introduction: Semantic role labeling: An introduction to the special issue. *Computational Linguistics*, 34(2):145–159.

Abelardo Carlos Martínez Lorenzo, Marco Maru, and Roberto Navigli. 2022. Fully-Semantic Parsing and

Generation: the BabelNet Meaning Representation. In *Proceedings of the 60th Annual Meeting of the Association for Computational Linguistics (Volume 1: Long Papers)*, pages 1727–1741, Dublin, Ireland. Association for Computational Linguistics.

Tom McCoy, Ellie Pavlick, and Tal Linzen. 2019. Right for the wrong reasons: Diagnosing syntactic heuristics in natural language inference. In *Proceedings of the 57th Annual Meeting of the Association for Computational Linguistics*, pages 3428–3448, Florence, Italy. Association for Computational Linguistics.

George A. Miller, Richard Beckwith, Christiane D. Fellbaum, Derek Gross, and Katherine J. Miller. 1990. Introduction to wordnet: An on-line lexical database. *International Journal of Lexicography*, 3:235–244.

Roberto Navigli. 2009. Word sense disambiguation: A survey. *ACM computing surveys (CSUR)*, 41(2):1–69.

Roberto Navigli, Michele Bevilacqua, Simone Conia, Dario Montagnini, and Francesco Cecconi. 2021. Ten years of babelnet: A survey. In *Proceedings of the Thirtieth International Joint Conference on Artificial Intelligence, IJCAI 2021, Virtual Event / Montreal, Canada, 19-27 August 2021*, pages 4559–4567. ijcai.org.

Roberto Navigli and Simone Paolo Ponzetto. 2012. Babelnet: The automatic construction, evaluation and application of a wide-coverage multilingual semantic network. *Artificial Intelligence*, 193:217–250.

Stephan Oepen, Omri Abend, Lasha Abzianidze, Johan Bos, Jan Hajic, Daniel Hershcovich, Bin Li, Tim O'Gorman, Nianwen Xue, and Daniel Zeman. 2020. MRP 2020: The second shared task on cross-framework and cross-lingual meaning representation parsing. In *Proceedings of the CoNLL 2020 Shared Task: Cross-Framework Meaning Representation Parsing*, pages 1–22, Online. Association for Computational Linguistics.

Stephan Oepen and Jan Tore Lønning. 2006. Discriminant-based MRS banking. In *Proceedings of the Fifth International Conference on Language Resources and Evaluation (LREC'06)*, Genoa, Italy. European Language Resources Association (ELRA).

Martha Palmer, Daniel Gildea, and Paul Kingsbury. 2005. The Proposition Bank: An annotated corpus of semantic roles. *Computational Linguistics*, 31(1):71–106.

Giovanni Paolini, Ben Athiwaratkun, Jason Krone, Jie Ma, Alessandro Achille, Rishita Anubhai, Cícero Nogueira dos Santos, Bing Xiang, and Stefano Soatto. 2021. Structured prediction as translation between augmented natural languages. In *9th International Conference on Learning Representations, ICLR 2021, Virtual Event, Austria, May 3-7, 2021*. OpenReview.net.

Matthew E. Peters, Mark Neumann, Mohit Iyyer, Matt Gardner, Christopher Clark, Kenton Lee, and Luke Zettlemoyer. 2018. Deep contextualized word representations. In *Proceedings of the 2018 Conference of the North American Chapter of the Association for Computational Linguistics: Human Language Technologies, Volume 1 (Long Papers)*, pages 2227–2237, New Orleans, Louisiana. Association for Computational Linguistics.

Luigi Procopio, Edoardo Barba, Federico Martelli, and Roberto Navigli. 2021a. Multimirror: Neural cross-lingual word alignment for multilingual word sense disambiguation. In *Proceedings of the Thirtieth International Joint Conference on Artificial Intelligence, IJCAI-21*, pages 3915–3921. International Joint Conferences on Artificial Intelligence Organization. Main Track.

Luigi Procopio, Rocco Tripodi, and Roberto Navigli. 2021b. SGL: Speaking the graph languages of semantic parsing via multilingual translation. In *Proceedings of the 2021 Conference of the North American Chapter of the Association for Computational Linguistics: Human Language Technologies*, pages 325–337, Online. Association for Computational Linguistics.

Xiao Pu, Nikolaos Pappas, James Henderson, and Andrei Popescu-Belis. 2018. Integrating Weakly Supervised Word Sense Disambiguation into Neural Machine Translation. *Transactions of the Association for Computational Linguistics*, 6:635–649.

Alexis Ross, Tongshuang Wu, Hao Peng, Matthew E. Peters, and Matt Gardner. 2022. Tailor: Generating and perturbing text with semantic controls. In *Proceedings of the 60th Annual Meeting of the Association for Computational Linguistics (Volume 1: Long Papers), ACL 2022, Dublin, Ireland, May 22-27, 2022*, pages 3194–3213. Association for Computational Linguistics.

Arka Sadhu, Tanmay Gupta, Mark Yatskar, Ram Nevatia, and Aniruddha Kembhavi. 2021. Visual semantic role labeling for video understanding. In *IEEE Conference on Computer Vision and Pattern Recognition, CVPR 2021, virtual, June 19-25, 2021*, pages 5589–5600. Computer Vision Foundation / IEEE.

Dan Shen and Mirella Lapata. 2007. Using semantic roles to improve question answering. In *Proceedings of the 2007 Joint Conference on Empirical Methods in Natural Language Processing and Computational Natural Language Learning (EMNLP-CoNLL)*, pages 12–21, Prague, Czech Republic. Association for Computational Linguistics.

Linfeng Song, Daniel Gildea, Yue Zhang, Zhiguo Wang, and Jinsong Su. 2019. Semantic neural machine translation using AMR. *Transactions of the Association for Computational Linguistics*, 7:19–31.

Aaron Steven White, Drew Reisinger, Keisuke Sakaguchi, Tim Vieira, Sheng Zhang, Rachel Rudinger,

Kyle Rawlins, and Benjamin Van Durme. 2016. Universal decompositional semantics on Universal Dependencies. In *Proceedings of the 2016 Conference on Empirical Methods in Natural Language Processing*, pages 1713–1723, Austin, Texas. Association for Computational Linguistics.

Gregor Wiedemann, Steffen Remus, Avi Chawla, and Chris Biemann. 2019. Does BERT make any sense? interpretable word sense disambiguation with contextualized embeddings. In *Proceedings of the 15th Conference on Natural Language Processing, KONVENS 2019, Erlangen, Germany, October 9-11, 2019*.

Nianwen Xue. 2008. Labeling Chinese predicates with semantic roles. *Computational Linguistics*, 34(2):225–255.

Dayu Yuan, Julian Richardson, Ryan Doherty, Colin Evans, and Eric Altendorf. 2016. Semi-supervised word sense disambiguation with neural models. In *Proceedings of COLING 2016, the 26th International Conference on Computational Linguistics: Technical Papers*, pages 1374–1385, Osaka, Japan. The COLING 2016 Organizing Committee.

Sheng Zhang, Xutai Ma, Kevin Duh, and Benjamin Van Durme. 2019. AMR parsing as sequence-to-graph transduction. In *Proceedings of the 57th Annual Meeting of the Association for Computational Linguistics*, pages 80–94, Florence, Italy. Association for Computational Linguistics.

Author Index

Association for Computational Linguistics
209 N. Eighth Street
Stroudsburg, Pennsylvania 18360

ISBN 978-1-7138-6313-7

Workshop on Scaling Up Multilingual Evaluation (SUMEval 2022)

Online
20 November 2022